Houghton Mifflin Science
DISCOVERYWORKS
TEACHING GUIDE / 3

D1298934

Roles of Living Things

Welcome

to Houghton Mifflin **Science DiscoveryWorks** — a science program that provides a balance of exciting hands-on activities and engaging content resources. **Science DiscoveryWorks** reflects our belief that effective science education gradually introduces students to the knowledge, methods, skills, and attitudes of scientists, while simultaneously recognizing and respecting the educational and developmental needs of all students.

HOUGHTON MIFFLIN

Boston • Atlanta • Dallas • Denver • Geneva, Illinois • Palo Alto • Princeton

WITHDRAWN
FIRELANDS COLLEGE
BGSU FIRELANDS LIBRARY
LIBRARY

Acknowledgments appear on pages A72, B82, C82, D70, E82, which constitute extensions of this copyright page.

Copyright © 2000 by Houghton Mifflin Company. All rights reserved.

No part of this work may be reproduced or transmitted in any form or by any means, electronic or mechanical, including photocopying or recording, or by any information storage or retrieval system without the prior written permission of Houghton Mifflin Company unless such copying is expressly permitted by federal copyright law. Address inquiries to School Permissions, 222 Berkeley Street, Boston, MA 02116.

Printed in the U.S.A.

Grade 3 One-Volume Teaching Guide   ISBN 0-618-00864-0   2 3 4 5 6 7 8 9-WEB-04 03 02 01 00

Grade 3 Modular Teaching Guides

Unit A: Life Cycles   ISBN 0-618-00292-8   3 4 5 6 7 8 9-WEB-04 03 02 01 00

Unit B: Sun, Moon, and Earth   ISBN 0-618-00293-6   3 4 5 6 7 8 9-WEB-04 03 02 01 00

Unit C: Matter, Energy, and Forces   ISBN 0-618-00294-4   3 4 5 6 7 8 9-WEB-04 03 02 01 00

Unit D: Earth's Resources   ISBN 0-618-00295-2   3 4 5 6 7 8 9-WEB-04 03 02 01 00

Unit E: Roles of Living Things   ISBN 0-618-00296-0   3 4 5 6 7 8 9-WEB-04 03 02 01 00

CURR
372.35
H35h
Gr.3
Teaching
Guide
Unit E

ABOUT THE PROGRAM

THE AUTHORS

Coming From Diverse Backgrounds, Meeting on Common Ground

William Badders

Elementary Science Teacher,
Cleveland Public Schools, Cleveland, OH

A 1992 Presidential Award winner, Mr. Badders teaches science to students in Grades K through 6. He was a member of the Working Group on Science Assessment Standards. He is a member of the Board of Directors of the National Science Teachers Association. He specializes in the biological and physical sciences.

Dr. Lowell J. Bethel

Professor of Science Education,
The University of Texas at Austin, Austin, TX

Dr. Bethel recently served as Program Director for Teacher Enhancement at the National Science Foundation. He specializes in the biological and physical sciences, urban and multicultural education, constructivism, and the development and evaluation of in-service science programs.

Dr. Victoria Fu

Professor of Child Development and Early Childhood
Education, Virginia Polytechnic Institute and
State University, Blacksburg, VA

Dr. Fu has extensive experience in teaching child development and teacher education. She has been involved, nationally and internationally, in teacher education initiatives based on qualitative inquiry. Her current research and writings focus on young children as learners and inquirers.

Donald Peck

Director (retired), The Center for Elementary Science,
Fairleigh Dickinson University, Madison, NJ

Mr. Peck's extensive experience in science education includes conducting more than 500 hands-on science workshops for elementary school teachers. He also was a K–12 science supervisor for 23 years. He specializes in the physical and earth sciences.

Dr. Carolyn Sumners

Director of Astronomy and Physical Sciences,
Houston Museum of Natural Science, Houston, TX

Dr. Sumners directs the museum's Burke Baker Planetarium, Challenger Learning Center, and technology camps. She also curates the museum's Welch Chemistry Hall, Fondren Discovery Place, and Arnold Hall of Space Sciences. She is project director for the Toys in Space program at the Johnson Space Center and is a published author of children's books.

Catherine Valentino

Author-in-Residence – Houghton Mifflin,
West Kingston, RI

Ms. Valentino has extensive experience as a classroom teacher, a curriculum coordinator, and a director of elementary education. In her current position, she specializes in developing educational materials that integrate inquiry-based learning and problem-solving skills in all of the content areas. At the University of Rhode Island she serves as Curriculum Advisor for SMILE (Science and Math Investigative Learning Experiences), an after-school enrichment program for students in Grades 4–12.

Reading Consultant

Dr. Peter Dewitz

Educational Consultant
Charlottesville, VA

Dr. Peter Dewitz is a reading expert who specializes in the comprehension of informational text. He was an elementary school teacher in Los Angeles before moving to college teaching and research at the University of Toledo and most recently at the University of Virginia. Currently Dr. Dewitz is working with various school districts to restructure reading instruction.

Sheltered English Consultant

Ronald Rohac

Faculty Member,
California State University-Long Beach, Long Beach, CA

Ron Rohac has been a classroom teacher for 22 years, with extensive background and experience in working with Limited English Proficient students. Mr. Rohac is currently a faculty member at California State University, Long Beach, and is a well-known consultant who creates staff development programs, classroom strategies, and program design for state departments and school districts all over the United States.

We believe . . .

As individuals we come from a variety of backgrounds, but as educators we meet on common ground. We share a vision of effective science education for all children. Our vision is based on these principles.

Our Principles

- Students learn science concepts most effectively through a balance of hands-on activities and solid content knowledge. We provide students with many opportunities to use science process skills and the methods of science through hands-on activities. In addition, we provide solid content resources to help students understand their hands-on exploration.

- In a world that is growing increasingly dependent on the contributions of science, scientific literacy is an important educational goal for all students. In this program we teach students to use science process skills, critical-thinking skills, and scientific reasoning skills to help develop scientific literacy.

- Assessment is an ongoing process that should be used to guide instruction. The variety of assessment in *DiscoveryWorks* enables teachers to tailor assessment to student needs and abilities.

- Science education is enhanced when based upon reliable educational standards that guide student attainment, curriculum content, and teaching practices. *Science DiscoveryWorks* is based on the Benchmarks for Science Literacy prepared by Project 2061, a long-term educational reform project of the American Association for the Advancement of Science, and the National Science Education Standards prepared by the National Research Council.

The Authors

Consultants & Reviewers

National Advisory Board

Dr. Glenn Berkheimer
Retired Prof. of Science Ed.
Michigan State University
East Lansing, MI

Andrea Bermúdez
Dir., Research Ctr. for Language
University of Houston-Clear Lake
Houston, TX

Pat Bowers
Prof., Ctr. for Math and Science
Education
University of North Carolina
Chapel Hill, NC

Bernard Bradley
Science Specialist
Newberry Math & Science Acad.
Chicago, IL

John Cunningham
Science Supervisor
East St. Louis School Dist. 189
East St. Louis, IL

Dr. Judy Dennison
K-12 Science Coordinator
Fulton County Schools
Atlanta, GA

Ronald Ellis
Assoc. Prof., City University of NY
Lehman College
Bronx, NY

Gilda Hester
Chap. 1 Math/Science Specialist
St. Louis Public Schools
St. Louis, MO

Carolyn Randolph
Science Supervisor
Lexington School District 2
West Columbia, SC

Josephine Scott
Supervisor, Multicultural Ed.
Columbus Public Schools
Columbus, OH

John Swang
Teacher
Mandeville Middle School
Mandeville, LA

Debbie Valdez
Teacher
Paul Revere Middle School
Houston, TX

Florencia R. Valenzuela
Technology Specialist
Cochise County Schools
Bisbee, AZ

Content Consultants

Dr. Carl Barrentine
Assoc. Prof., Humanities and Bio.
University of North Dakota
Grand Forks, ND

Dr. Nadine G. Barlow
Dir. of the Robinson Observatory
Physics Department
University of Central Florida
Orlando, FL

Dr. Glenn Berkheimer
Prof. Emeritus of Science Ed.
Michigan State University
East Lansing, MI

Dr. Bonnie Buratti
Jet Propulsion Lab
California Institute of Technology
Pasadena, CA

Dr. Dennis Cheek
Dir. of Info. Serv. and Research
Rhode Island Department of Ed.
Providence, RI

Dr. Linda Cronin-Jones
Assoc. Prof., Doctoral Faculty
University of Florida
Gainesville, FL

Dr. Thomas A. Davies
Research Scientist
Ocean Drilling Program
Texas A&M University
College Station, TX

Dr. Ruth Eshleman
Professor of Nutrition
University of Rhode Island
West Kingston, RI

David G. Futch, Ph.D.
Assoc. Prof., Dept. of Biology
San Diego State University
San Diego, CA

Dr. Orin G. Gelderloos
Department of Natural Sciences
University of Michigan-Dearborn
Dearborn, MI

Gretchen Gillis
Geologist
Maxus Exploration Company
Dallas, TX

Dr. John Gohagan
Early Detection Branch
National Cancer Institute
Rockville, MD

Dr. Fern Gotfried
Pediatrician
Cedar Knolls, NJ

Dr. Harry Hendon
NOAA/CIRES
Climate Diagnostic Center
Boulder, CO

Donald Lisowy
Manager of Teacher Programs
New York Botanical Gardens
New York, NY

Dr. Tom Murphree
Department of Meteorology
Naval Postgraduate School
Monterey, CA

Dr. Suzanne O'Connell
Department of Earth and
Environmental Sciences
Wesleyan University
Middletown, CT

Dr. Wendell Potter
Department of Physics
University of California at Davis
Davis, CA

Dr. Betty Preece
Engineer and Physicist
Indialantic, FL

Dr. Yaakow Shecter
Professor, Department of
Biological Sciences
City University of New York
Lehman College
Bronx, NY

Dr. Jennifer Specker
Prof. of Oceanography
Biological Sciences
University of Rhode Island
Narragansett, RI

Dr. Janet Sisterson
Cyclotron Laboratory
Harvard University
Cambridge, MA

Dr. Nina Surawicz
Director, Student Health Center
Arizona State University
Tempe, AZ

Dr. Beverly Taylor
Assistant Professor
Miami University, Hamilton
Hamilton, OH

Dr. Dominick Valentino
Professor of Psychobiology
University of Rhode Island
West Kingston, RI

Claudia Viehland
Biochemist, Research Technical
Service
Sigma Chemical Company
St. Louis, MO

Dr. Sidney White
Dept. of Geological Sciences
Ohio State University
Columbus, OH

Multicultural Consultants

Eduardo Aparicio
Spanish Editor and Translator
Miami, FL

Albert Carranco
Honors Chemistry Teacher
Roy Miller High School
Corpus Christi, TX

Ronald Ellis
Associate Professor
City University of New York
Lehman College
Bronx, NY

John Kibler
InterAmerica Intercultural
Training Institute
Des Plaines, IL

Chin Kim
LA Unified School District
Los Angeles, CA

Dr. Ngoc-Diep T. Nguyen
Director, Bilingual and
Multicultural Program
Schaumburg, IL

Carolyn Randolph
Science Supervisor
Lexington School District 2
West Columbia, SC

Josephine Scott
Supervisor, Multicultural Ed.
Columbus Public Schools
Columbus, OH

Florencia R. Valenzuela
Technology Specialist
Cochise County Schools
Bisbee, AZ

Teacher Reviewers

Lisa Acy
Louis Agassiz Elementary Sch.
Cleveland, OH

Renee Addison
Northwestern Lehigh Middle Sch.
New Tripoli, PA

Leslie Armstrong
Laura S. Ward Elementary
Chicago, IL

Leslye Auerbach
Banyan Elementary
Sunrise, FL

Judith Ball
Coordinator for
Math/Science/Health
School District U46
Elgin, IL

Karen R. Bishop
Ferron Elementary School
Ferron, UT

Jean Blackshear
Fred A. Toomer Elementary Sch.
Atlanta, GA

Frank A. Bodgen, Jr.
Carver Elementary
Henderson, NC

Bonnie Bohrer
Brookview Elementary School
Brook Park, OH

Robert L. Burtch
1990 Presidential Award winner
Batavia Middle School
Batavia, IL

Martha Christine
Calypso Elementary School
Bethlehem, PA

Mary Eve Corrigan
The Columbus Academy
Gahanna, OH

Patty Dadonna
Hollywood Elementary
Hollywood, FL

John S. Detrick
Emeritus Dept. Chair of
Mathematics, holder of the
McElroy Chair of Mathematics
The Columbus Academy
Gahanna, OH

Robert C. Dixon
National Center to Improve the
Tools of Educators (NCITE)
University of Oregon, College of
Education
Eugene, OR

Denise Pitts-Downing
James Elverson Middle School
Philadelphia, PA

Michaeline A. Dudas
Science and Math Instructional
Support/Consultant
Northbrook, IL

William Dudrow
The Columbus Academy
Gahanna, OH

Terri Dyer
Lake Weston Elementary
Orlando, FL

Barbara Elliott
1990 Presidential Award winner
Ray E. Kilmer Elementary School
Colorado Springs, CO

Fred Fabry
Retired teacher of Geology and
Biology
Deerfield High School
Deerfield, IL

Debbie Fitzpatrick
School 14
Clifton, NJ

Rhea Foster
Anderson Park Elementary Sch.
Atlanta, GA

Audrey Ann Fredrick
James Bowie Elementary
San Antonio, TX

Linda Froschauer
1993 Presidential Award winner
Weston Middle School
Weston, CT

Joanne Gallagher
Tamarac Middle School
Melrose, NY

Donna Green
Beauclerc Elementary
Jacksonville, FL

Marlene Gregor
Elem. Science Consultant
Bloomington, IL

Kim Grimme
Ponderosa Elementary
Sunnyvale, CA

Becca Stein Gutwirth
Florence M. Gaudineer School
Springfield, NJ

William L. Handy, Jr.
Parkland School District
Orefield, PA

Beverly Hanrahan
Franconia Elementary School
Souderton, PA

Renee Harris
Northwestern Lehigh Mid. Sch.
New Tripoli, PA

Patricia Heavens
Dunbar Elementary
East St. Louis, IL

Rhonda Hicks
James Elverson Middle School
Philadelphia, PA

Sr. Marie Patrice
Hoare, S.L.
Loretto Middle School
El Paso, TX

Nancy Hronkin
Forest Park Elementary
Crystal Falls, MI

Gail Hurst
Dr. Philips Elementary
Orlando, FL

Lester Y. Ichinose, Ph.D.
Evanston, IL

Mace A. Ishida, Ph.D.
Diversity and Ed. Consultant
Blacklick, OH

Kristine D. Jackson
Belleville, IL

Pearline A. James
W. F. Slaton Elementary School
Atlanta, GA

Evette Jones
Grover Cleveland Elementary
Philadelphia, PA

Charlene Kalinski
Gilvert Cuellar Elementary
Dallas, TX

Sr. Sharon Kassing, S.L.
St. Pius Catholic School
Kirkwood, MO

Jill Kersh
Bullock Elementary
Garland, TX

Gail Kirkland
Hiawassee Elementary
Orlando, FL

John Kibler
InterAmerica Intercultural
Training Institute
Des Plaines, IL

Jennifer Kimble
Rogers Elementary
Dallas, TX

Diane Landschoot
John N. C. Stockton Elementary
Jacksonville, FL

Bonnie Lawhorn
Evening Street Elementary
Worthington, OH

Sharon Lempner
R. G. Jones School
Cleveland, OH

Barbara Leonard
1992 Presidential Award winner
Heritage Elementary School
Pueblo, CO

Gus Liss
Young Elementary School
Burlington, NJ

Jo Ann Liss
Intervale School
Parsippany, NJ

Marlenn Maicki
1990 Presidential Award winner
Detroit Country Day School
Bloomfield Hills, MI

Lynn Malok
Spring Garden Elementary Sch.
Bethlehem, PA

Barbara Mecker
Rockwood South Middle Sch.
St. Louis, MO

Leonardo Melton
Fred A. Toomer Elementary Sch.
Atlanta, GA

Bonniejean Meyer
Tremont Elementary School
Cleveland, OH

Laura Mobbett
Huff School
Mountain View, CA

Dr. Suzanne Moore
L. L. Hotchkiss Elementary Sch.
Dallas, TX

Kathy Morton
Christ the King School
Atlanta, GA

Debora Multisano
Clair-Mel Elementary
Tampa, FL

Dr. Ngoc-Diep T. Nguyen
Director, Bilingual and
Multicultural Program
Schaumburg, IL

Michael O'Shea
R. G. Jones School
Cleveland, OH

Wendy Peterson
Harvey Rice Elementary School
Cleveland, OH

Filomena Poli-Aleman
Clifton Public School #4
Clifton, NJ

Alexandra Pond
Science Coordinator
North Shore School
Chicago, IL

Herb Quon
Spangler Elementary
Milipitas, CA

Terry Ramirez
Lackland City Elementary
San Antonio, TX

José Salas
Hooper Ave. School
Los Angeles, CA

Erika Silverman
Public School 41
Bronx, NY

Debi Sitkoski
Forest Park Elementary
Crystal Falls, MI

Chris Spigarelli
Forest Park Elementary
Crystal Falls, MI

Christine Spinner
Parkview Elementary
Parma, OH

Jean Ann Strillacci
Kennedy Elementary School
Succasunna, NJ

Laura Swanson
WATTS Intermediate School
Burlington City, NJ

Arthur F. Tobia
Public School 41
Bronx, NY

Laura Turner
Clover Flat Elementary
Boulevard, CA

Nancy Vibeto
1993 Presidential Award winner
Jim Hill Middle School
Minot, ND

Kathy Westbrook
Bluffsview Elementary
Columbus, OH

Sandra Wilson
McKinley Elementary School
Abington, PA

Bonita Wylie
Minnewashta Elementary
Excelsior, MN

THE SCOPE OF THE PROGRAM
An Overview of Concepts and Themes

	KINDERGARTEN	GRADE 1	GRADE 2
Life Science 	**UNIT A Characteristics of Living Things** Classification of objects as living or nonliving; basic needs and stages of growth of living things **Themes:** *Systems, Constancy and Change*	**UNIT A Kinds of Living Things** The similarities and differences between plants and animals; classifying plants and animals according to one characteristic; life cycles of plants and animals **Theme:** *Systems*	**UNIT A Interactions of Living Things** The needs of living things; plant and animal adaptations to various habitats; the effect of living things and natural forces on environments **Themes:** *Constancy and Change, Models*
	UNIT E Body Parts Identification of internal and external body parts; the functions and importance of individual body parts, including the hands, bones, muscles, heart, stomach, and brain **Themes:** *Systems, Models*	**UNIT E Keeping Fit and Healthy** The importance of good nutrition, exercise, sleep, and proper hygiene; the food pyramid and a healthful diet **Themes:** *Systems, Constancy and Change*	**UNIT E What Makes Me Sick** How germs cause illness; how illnesses spread; prevention of illnesses and injuries; how to stay healthy **Themes:** *Systems, Scale*
Physical Science 	**UNIT B Exploring With the Senses** Using the senses to observe the physical characteristics of objects; grouping objects by their physical characteristics **Theme:** *Systems*	**UNIT C Magnets** The properties of magnets; magnetic force; magnetic fields; temporary magnets; magnets and compasses **Themes:** *Systems, Scale*	**UNIT B Energy and Motion** Characteristics of light; measuring motion; how forces affect motion; sound waves, pitch, and volume; heat energy and uses of natural resources for heat **Themes:** *Constancy and Change, Scale*
	UNIT D Pushes and Pulls Different ways things move; pushes and pulls; surfaces; directional motion **Themes:** *Systems, Models*		**UNIT D Solids, Liquids, and Gases** Properties of solids, liquids, and gases; the changing of materials from one state to another **Theme:** *Constancy and Change*
Earth Science 	**UNIT C Looking at the Earth and Sky** Landforms; daytime sky and the sun; changing seasons and the weather; the moon and the stars **Themes:** *Constancy and Change, Scale*	**UNIT B Weather and Seasons** Factors that affect the weather; seasonal weather changes; how people, plants, and animals respond to weather conditions **Theme:** *Constancy and Change*	**UNIT C Changes Over Time** Characteristics of different dinosaurs; how trace fossils and fossil remains provide clues about the earth's history; changes in the day and night sky; daily and seasonal weather patterns **Themes:** *Models, Scale, Constancy and Change*
		**UNIT D Earth's Land and Water** Properties of soil and rocks; how water and soil mix; how water flows; recycling soil, water, and rocks **Themes:** *Systems, Models*	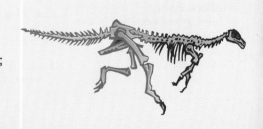

> *The science that all students are expected to learn is defined so that students have sufficient time to develop a deep understanding of essential scientific ideas rather than superficial acquaintance with many isolated facts.*
>
> National Science Education Standards

GRADE 3	GRADE 4	GRADE 5	GRADE 6
UNIT A Life Cycles Stages in the life cycles of animals and plants; changes in animals and plants as they mature; inherited traits; ways that animals and plants survive **Theme:** *Models*	**UNIT C Classifying Living Things** Classification of living things; characteristics of different animal and plant groups; basic needs of living things; adaptations that help living things meet their needs. **Theme:** *Systems*	**UNIT A Systems in Living Things** Life processes of plants and animals; structure of plant and animal cells; human digestive, respiratory, circulatory, and excretory systems; life cycles of plants and animals **Theme:** *Systems*	**UNIT A Cells and Microbes** Structure and life processes of cells, including mitosis; protists and fungi; bacteria and viruses **Theme:** *Models*
UNIT E Roles of Living Things The needs of living things in relation to their environments; how living things adapt to their environments, change them, and respond to them **Theme:** *Constancy and Change*		**UNIT D Populations and Ecosystems** Dynamic interactions of living and nonliving things in an ecosystem; how energy and matter flow through an ecosystem; biomes; biodiversity **Theme:** *Systems*	**UNIT D Continuity of Life** Asexual reproduction; sexual reproduction, including meiosis; inherited and acquired traits; evolution, including evidence for evolution and evolutionary processes **Theme:** *Constancy and Change*
UNIT C Matter, Energy, and Forces Properties, states, and changes in matter; forms of energy and how heat energy moves and changes matter; forces and machines **Theme:** *Systems*	**UNIT B Properties of Matter** Physical properties; states; effects of heat loss or gain and of physical and chemical changes **Theme:** *Scale*	**UNIT C Matter and Energy** Properties of matter; states of matter; elements, compounds, and mixtures; forms of energy; energy transfer; changes in energy; changes in matter **Theme:** *Models*	**UNIT C The Nature of Matter** Physical and chemical properties; elements, compounds, mixtures; physical and chemical changes; acids and bases; atomic structure **Theme:** *Scale*
	UNIT D Magnetism and Electricity Properties of magnets; forms of electrical energy; electric circuits; sources of electric current; how electric current is changed into useful energy **Theme:** *Models*	**UNIT F Light and Sound** Properties of light; lenses and their uses; color; properties of sound; the sense of hearing; controlling, recording, and transmitting sound **Theme:** *Models*	**UNIT F Forces and Motion** Characteristics of motion; gravity; measuring changes in motion; friction; action-reaction forces; how forces affect the motion of objects **Theme:** *Scale*
UNIT B Sun, Moon, and Earth The physical features of the Sun and Moon; the rotation and revolution of Earth and the Moon; planets of the solar system; Earth's seasonal changes; eclipses **Theme:** *Scale*	**UNIT A Earth's Land** How moving water, wind, and ice shape the land; natural resources and conservation efforts; consequences of producing and disposing of trash **Theme:** *Constancy and Change*	**UNIT B The Solar System and Beyond** The night sky; how astronomers learn about space; the solar system; stars and galaxies; survival in space **Theme:** *Scale*	**UNIT B The Changing Earth** Theory of plate tectonics; the movement of continents; the formation of mountains; earthquakes and volcanoes **Theme:** *Models*
UNIT D Earth's Resources The importance of air, water, and land; renewable, nonrenewable, and inexhaustible resources; uses and protection of Earth's air, water, and land; forces that change Earth's surface; properties of soils **Theme:** *Constancy and Change*	**UNIT E Weather and Climate** Earth's atmosphere; effects of changes in the air on weather; the water cycle; weather patterns and predictions; seasonal weather changes and climate **Theme:** *Constancy and Change*	**UNIT E The Solid Earth** Properties and uses of minerals and rocks; the rock cycle; Earth's structure; fossils as clues to the age of rocks; the formation of crustal features, such as mountains **Theme:** *Constancy and Change*	**UNIT E Oceanography** Contents and properties of ocean water; features and exploration of the ocean floor; currents, waves, and tides; resources from the ocean; ocean pollution **Theme:** *Systems*

TEACHING MODEL

Flexibility is an important feature of the Science DiscoveryWorks *program. Although the* Teaching Guide *suggests ways in which you can use the program components to organize and guide each lesson, you can adapt these suggestions or develop your own teaching strategies. The model shown here is one way of teaching a unit.*

Unit Opener

The *Unit Opener* headline and photograph highlight a scientific phenomenon that occurs in a real-world setting. The opener can be used to engage students' interest in the topic to be studied.

Introduction Have students read the introductory paragraph and discuss what they know about the science topic.

Think Like a Scientist Have students review some of the questions they will investigate in the unit and then have them suggest some of their own questions.

Chapter Opener

The *Chapter Opener* photograph and introductory text focuses on people using science and the role of science in culture and the arts. The photo and text can be used as a discussion starter for the chapter topics.

Warm-up Activity Use the suggested activity in the *Teaching Guide* to motivate interest.

Home-School Connection Extend science learning to the home with easy-to-do activities.

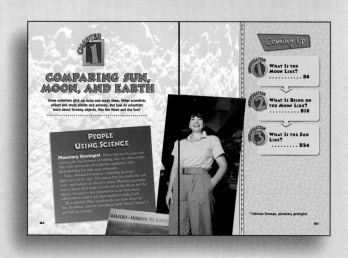

Investigations

The *Investigations*, which form the heart of the **Science DiscoveryWorks** program, are made up of two types of student pages—*Activities* and *Resources*.

Activities Provide hands-on experiences for students that make subsequent readings more meaningful. These experiences form the basis for conceptual development.

- Use the suggested baseline assessment in the *Teaching Guide* to activate prior knowledge.

- Have students record their observations, data, and responses in their *Science Notebooks* as they do the Activities.

- Have students go beyond the basic Activities, using suggestions found in *Investigate Further* boxes. These suggestions include both hands-on and CD-ROM activities.

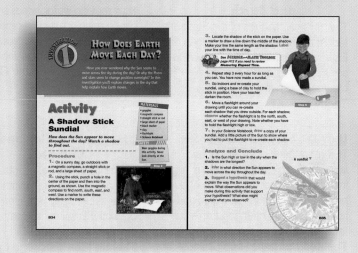

Resources Provide solid science content that reinforces and extends the concepts that students explored in the Activities.

- In addition to regular text material, these resources use a variety of approaches that include Time Capsules; How It Works; Science, Technology & Society; and Global Views.
- Use the *Unit Project Links* and the associated *Science Notebook* pages to provide students with an opportunity to apply their knowledge and understanding.

Close the Investigation Assess student understanding of key science concepts and vocabulary.

- Have students write the answers to the *Think It–Write It* questions in their *Science Notebooks*.
- Use the *Investigation Review* found in the *Ongoing Assessment* section of the *Teacher Resource Book*.

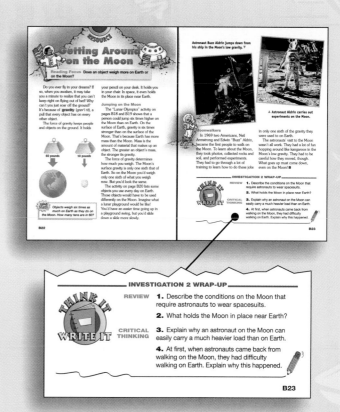

Reflect and Evaluate

The *Reflect and Evaluate* page at the end of each chapter helps students reinforce and review the concepts developed in the chapter.

- Have students reflect on their understanding by answering the questions in their *Science Notebooks*.
- Use the *Performance Assessment* suggestion, with accompanying scoring rubric, found in the *Teaching Guide,* to further assess student understanding.

Unit Wrap-up

The *Unit Wrap-up* page at the end of each unit reinforces student understanding of the scientific process.

Think Like a Scientist Have students use these suggestions to investigate a question on their own, using scientific methods.

Writing in Science Extend communication skills in a science context.

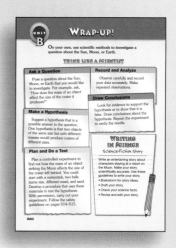

TECHNOLOGY RESOURCES

Science DiscoveryWorks offers a wide variety of technology resources that provide alternative ways of presenting and developing science concepts. These resources also provide students with opportunities to use technological tools and to develop an understanding of how technology contributes to advances in science.

Computer Resources

For the Teacher

DiscoveryWorks Lesson Planner A lesson planning CD-ROM tool allows you to customize the order of units, choose the lessons you plan to teach, and select the number and lengths of periods taught per week.

DiscoveryWorks Test Generator This CD-ROM contains ready-made chapter, unit, and standardized-format tests, in English and Spanish, that can be easily customized to meet your needs. Choose from multiple-choice and free-response questions.

For the Student

Science Processor CD-ROM This software provides an interactive, child-centered learning approach. The CD-ROM provides Investigations that replace or enhance the Investigations in the student book. The software also includes a Science Workshop in which students can explore and create in an open environment, as well as a customized encyclopedia. On-screen tools include a Spreadsheet, a Grapher, a Writer, a Painter, a Calculator, and a Timer.

Best of the Net This CD-ROM program provides guided Internet experiences in Life Science, Earth Science, Physical Science, and the Human Body. It requires no Internet connection.

For the Teacher and the Student

www.eduplace.com Visit Houghton Mifflin's Web site for a rich environment of interactive on-line teacher resources and student activities. Internet Field Trips and Unit Project Links referenced in the Student Edition are supported with up-to-date links. Included are professional and home resources, Kids' Clubhouse science activities, Teacher's Discussion Forums, and an area for classes to share their project results.

Video/Audio Resources

Videotapes "Bill Nye the Science Guy" videos are correlated to units throughout *DiscoveryWorks*. Ways to use these exciting videos to enhance or extend science concepts are suggested on the Using Technology pages that precede each unit.

Activity Video Lab Video demonstrations aid you in preparing, conducting, and concluding activities from *DiscoveryWorks*.

Books on Tape Audiotapes, in English and Spanish, enable students to follow along as the Student Edition is read aloud. These tapes help meet the individual needs of auditory learners, bilingual and ESL students, and challenged readers.

MEETING INDIVIDUAL NEEDS

We know that classroom educators today are very conscious of trying to meet the needs of a diverse student population. Houghton Mifflin Science DiscoveryWorks provides varied activities throughout the program designed to help you meet these needs.

Students Acquiring English

These activities are intended for use with students who are just learning the English language.

Gifted and Talented

These activities are appropriate for students who can think creatively and work independently on more challenging tasks.

Inclusion

These activities are intended for students with mental or physical disabilities who might benefit from alternative learning strategies.

Early Finishers

These activities can be used with students who complete the basic material earlier than the rest of the students.

For Extra Help

These activities provide additional help for students who are having difficulty understanding the concept of the lesson.

Learning Styles

Additionally, we realize that learning styles vary from student to student and even vary for a given student on different topics. Therefore, we have provided Activities that use the following learning styles to enable students to learn in ways that are most comfortable to them.

- **LINGUISTIC**
- **VISUAL/SPATIAL**
- **LOGICAL/MATHEMATICAL**
- **KINESTHETIC**
- **AUDITORY**

CONCEPT MAPS

Helping Students Organize Data

Houghton Mifflin *Science DiscoveryWorks* uses concept maps throughout the program to help students identify, organize, and process science information. These maps can be used to enhance student understanding by presenting processes and relationships visually.

KWL Chart

KWL charts help students form purposes for reading. The name of the concept being studied goes at the top of the chart. The first column is for recording what students know about the concept, and the second column is for recording what they want to know about it. In the last column, students record what they've learned after they have completed the unit.

Topic	The Solar System		
K What you know	**W** What you want to know	**L** What you learned
Earth revolves around the Sun. There are other planets in our solar system.	What are the other planets? Do other planets have moons?	

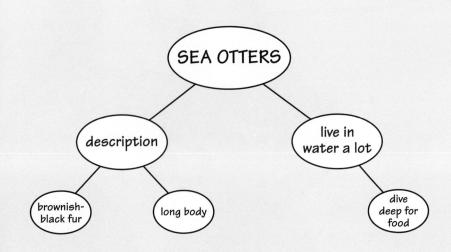

Webs

Webs can be used to show main ideas and subordinate ideas as well as part-whole relationships. The central large circle is for showing the main idea or concept. Smaller circles are for showing subordinate ideas.

Venn Diagram

A Venn diagram is an excellent way to compare and contrast things, such as a robin and a cardinal. Characteristics both birds share, such as wings and feathers, are listed in the overlapping parts of the two circles. Unique characteristics are listed in the non-overlapping parts of the circles.

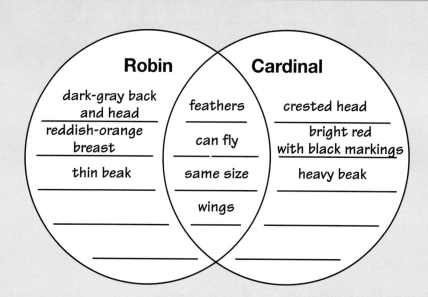

Sequence Chart

A sequence chart can be used to clarify the steps of a process or a chain of events. Each step is recorded in its own box, and the boxes are connected by arrows. In some cases, the last step in a process leads back to the first step. The chart then becomes a representation of a cycle.

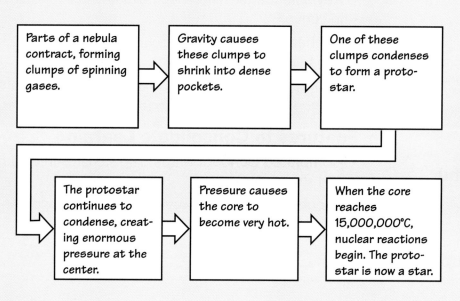

Cause and Effect

A cause-and-effect chart shows the relationship between causes and effects. Sometimes you may want to show how multiple causes lead to one effect. At other times you may want to show how one cause leads to several effects. You may also want to show a chain of causes and effects.

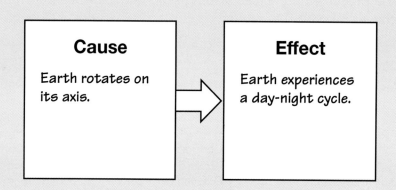

READING IN THE CONTENT AREA

Houghton Mifflin's Science DiscoveryWorks *helps make science concepts and informational text accessible to all students by providing students with opportunities to practice and apply reading skills and strategies.*

Improving Reading Comprehension

Science DiscoveryWorks recognizes that students can sometimes have difficulty reading informational text. Therefore, the development of *DiscoveryWorks* focused on creating a program that helps students read purposefully and strategically.

Features to Build Prior Knowledge

- **Concept Map Transparencies** preview important chapter ideas and their relationships.
- **Support Terms** (words that present problems for some students, especially those acquiring English) are identified in the *Teaching Guide* so that you can help students before they begin reading.
- **Concrete Hands-on Activities** help students understand concepts before they read.

Features to Make Reading Purposeful

- **KWL Activities** at the start of each unit help students inquire as they read and study.
- The **Reading Focus** question at the beginning of each Resource helps set a purpose for reading.

Features to Maximize Comprehension

- **Key science terms** are highlighted and explained in context.
- **Subheads** within each Resource divide the text into manageable sections.
- **Photos, illustrations,** and **charts** present concepts, processes, and relationships graphically.

Features to Consolidate Learning

- **Completed Concept Maps** help students integrate and study new ideas.
- **Vocabulary Masters** provide additional support for the chapter science terms.

Using Reading Skills Pages

At the end of each unit, a *Using Reading Skills* page gives students an additional opportunity to apply and practice a particular reading skill, using science informational text. The table below shows the set of skills that are developed across Grades 3 through 6 in *Science DiscoveryWorks*.

Unit	Grade 3	Grade 4	Grade 5	Grade 6
Unit A	Finding the Main Idea	Main Idea and Details	Main Idea and Details	Detecting the Sequence
Unit B	Drawing Conclusions	Cause and Effect	Drawing Conclusions	Main Idea and Details
Unit C	Detecting the Sequence	Compare and Contrast	Cause and Effect	Drawing Conclusions
Unit D	Cause and Effect	Drawing Conclusions	Summarizing	Cause and Effect
Unit E	Compare and Contrast	Detecting the Sequence	Detecting the Sequence	Compare and Contrast
Unit F			Compare and Contrast	Summarizing

INTEGRATING SCIENCE & MATH

Since mathematics frequently supports or forms the basis for scientific ideas, students often use their math skills as they study science. Science DiscoveryWorks, therefore, provides a variety of opportunities for students to apply, practice, and improve their math skills and knowledge.

Applying and Practicing Math Skills

It is often helpful to know exactly where math can be found in a science lesson. The icons below, which appear in the Student Edition, will help you and your students see and better use the connections that naturally exist between science and math.

Using Math You will find the *Using Math* feature throughout the Resources. This feature is usually a special "math caption" that asks students to use the data presented in drawings, graphs, or other visuals. For example, students may be asked to use computational skills, compare data, estimate, and apply other math skills.

Math Hint This feature is found throughout the Activities. These hints are included in procedural steps in Activities to assist students with the math that is needed in order to do the Activity successfully.

Science and Math Toolbox This section of the Student Edition provides instruction in using science equipment and reviews the math skills that are needed to do the Activities successfully. The Science and Math Toolbox varies by grade level so that skills and tools may be introduced at the appropriate time. Students can use these pages to review measurement techniques, graphs, calculators, and other skills and tools. The Toolbox is referenced in Activities where a particular skill or tool is needed.

Using Math Skills Pages

At the end of each unit, a *Using Math Skills* page gives students an additional opportunity to apply and practice a particular math skill in the context of science content. The table below shows the set of skills that are developed across Grades 3 through 6 in *Science DiscoveryWorks*.

Unit	Grade 3	Grade 4	Grade 5	Grade 6
Unit A	Analyze Data	Circle Graph	Line Graph	Analyze Data
Unit B	Time Measurement	Volume	Analyze Data	Bar Graph
Unit C	Bar Graph	Analyze Data	Equations and Formulas	Line Graph
Unit D	Circle Graph	Bar Graph	Circle Graph	Analyze Data
Unit E	Analyze Data	Line Graph	Bar Graph	Circle Graph
Unit F			Analyze Data	Equations and Formulas

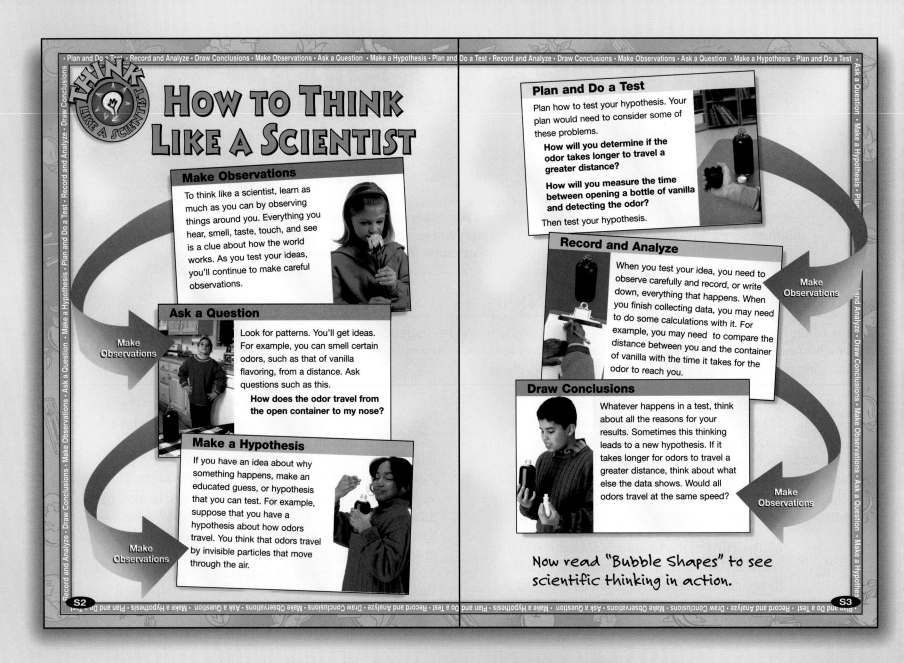

HOW DO SCIENTISTS STUDY NATURE?

What discoveries and inventions have had the greatest impact on people's lives? Antibiotics? Cell biology? The structure of matter? The printing press? Computer technology? Although all of these would be nominated, most people would not identify scientific thinking as a great invention. Yet this unique process for building knowledge has led to many discoveries. What makes this process such a powerful tool?

Exploring Nature

Until the seventeenth century, most people accepted untested explanations of events in nature. Myths and superstitions were often part of such explanations. Most people thought that Earth was at the center of the universe. They believed that the Sun, Moon, planets, and stars circled Earth. Although some scientists had hypothesized that Earth circled the Sun, it took an invention—the telescope—and the inquiring mind of a great scientist, Galileo Galilei, to provide evidence that supported this hypothesis.

Scientific Revolution

In 1609, Galileo peered through his primitive telescope at the planet Jupiter and *observed* what appeared to be tiny "stars" in a straight line near the giant planet. As he studied the planet for many nights, he was amazed to discover that the stars moved, yet stayed close to Jupiter. He *questioned* what these points of light could be. After *recording* the position of the stars each night and *analyzing* his records, Galileo *concluded* that the tiny lights must be Jupiter's moons. Galileo's discovery contradicted the common thinking of the day—that all heavenly bodies orbited Earth. And his evidence paved the way for popular acceptance of a revolutionary new way of understanding nature—scientific thinking.

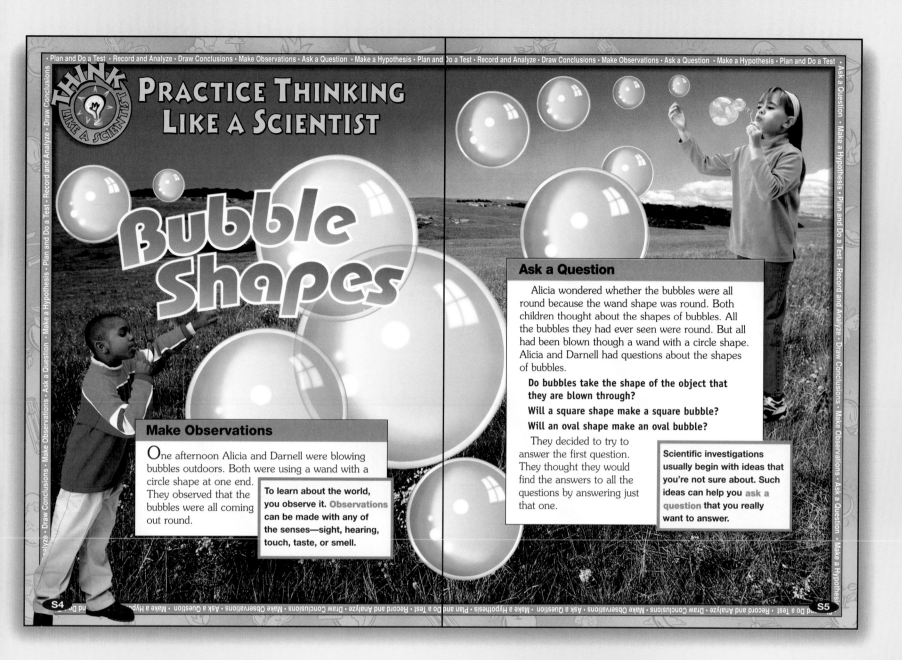

PRACTICE THINKING LIKE A SCIENTIST

Bubble Shapes

Make Observations

One afternoon Alicia and Darnell were blowing bubbles outdoors. Both were using a wand with a circle shape at one end. They observed that the bubbles were all coming out round.

To learn about the world, you observe it. Observations can be made with any of the senses—sight, hearing, touch, taste, or smell.

Ask a Question

Alicia wondered whether the bubbles were all round because the wand shape was round. Both children thought about the shapes of bubbles. All the bubbles they had ever seen were round. But all had been blown though a wand with a circle shape. Alicia and Darnell had questions about the shapes of bubbles.

Do bubbles take the shape of the object that they are blown through?

Will a square shape make a square bubble?

Will an oval shape make an oval bubble?

They decided to try to answer the first question. They thought they would find the answers to all the questions by answering just that one.

Scientific investigations usually begin with ideas that you're not sure about. Such ideas can help you ask a question that you really want to answer.

WHAT IS SCIENTIFIC THINKING?

Scientific thinking, also commonly called "scientific inquiry" or "the scientific method," is not a single method with a set number of orderly steps. It is a flexible process for both asking and answering questions about nature. Scientific thinking involves:

- Using all of the senses to make careful observations

- Asking specific questions about those observations that can be answered by using the tools of science

- Forming hypotheses that explain what is observed

- Testing these hypotheses through experiments and other tests and gathering and recording data

- Analyzing and drawing conclusions from the data

- Asking new questions, making new observations, and forming new hypotheses based on those findings

In school, students can learn how to use the process of scientific thinking in their daily lives. Students can also discover the vast body of knowledge that scientists, using that same process, have uncovered.

Scientific inquiry is dependent on critical-thinking skills. Scientists analyze nature in their attempts to understand and explain how nature works. This often involves breaking a phenomenon down (mentally and physically) into smaller and smaller parts to understand how the parts relate. Scientists also employ synthesis in their work—putting together pieces of the puzzle that is nature.

Scientific thinking also involves keeping an open mind about ideas. A tendency to want to investigate for oneself, rather than to accept the explanations of others, also characterizes scientific thinking.

Make a Hypothesis

Alicia and Darnell had an idea that blowing a bubble through a square wand would make a square bubble. They thought that an oval bubble would come from an oval-shaped wand. They both thought the shape of a wand would make a bubble of that same shape. So they made that their hypothesis.

Darnell wanted to know if the bubbles would come out square if the wand shape was square. Alicia was eager to learn if a wand with an oval shape would make an oval-shaped bubble.

When you use what you've observed to suggest a possible answer to your question, you're making a **hypothesis**. Make sure that your hypothesis is an idea that you can test. If you can't test your hypothesis, try changing it.

Plan and Do a Test

Later that day Alicia and Darnell planned how they would test their hypothesis. They decided to make different shaped wands for blowing bubbles. They used a length of straight wire to make a square-shaped wand. With a second length of wire they made an oval-shaped wand. They already had the bubble mixture, so they began their test.

One way to try out your hypothesis is to use a **test** called a **controlled experiment**. The setups in this kind of experiment are identical in all ways except one. The one difference is the **variable**. In Alicia and Darnell's experiment the variable is the shape of the bubble wand.

WHERE IS THE EVIDENCE?

With which of the following statements would your students agree? *Friday the 13th is an unlucky day. In a championship game, the home team has an advantage. Studying with the television on doesn't affect learning. If five coin tosses in a row show heads, the next toss is more likely to be tails.* To a scientist, each of these statements can be considered a testable *hypothesis.*

Gathering Data

Which hypotheses are supported by evidence and which are just unsupported opinions? There are many ways to test a hypothesis. Some involve gathering data and analyzing it. For example, is Friday the 13th really an "unlucky" day? A scientist would start by carefully defining certain terms and gathering information. What does the word *unlucky* mean in measurable terms? How many times has Friday

occurred on the 13th of the month? Are there more unlucky events on Friday the 13th than on the 13th day of the month when that day doesn't land on a Friday? By analyzing this data, a scientist could draw reasonable conclusions about whether the data supported the hypothesis that Friday the 13th was "unlucky."

A Controlled Test

Sometimes a hypothesis is best tested in a carefully controlled experiment. To discover if studying with the television on affects grades, scientists would compare students' learning scores under two conditions—an experimental condition in which the television is on and a control condition in which it is not. Again, data would be gathered and analyzed to determine if the hypothesis is supported or not. And the experiment would be repeated to verify the results.

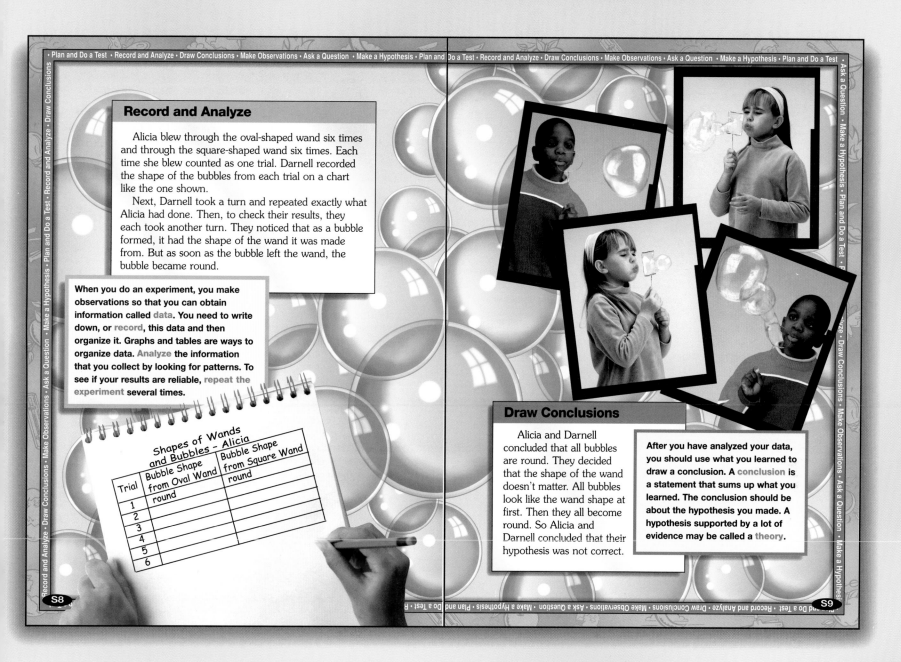

Record and Analyze

Alicia blew through the oval-shaped wand six times and through the square-shaped wand six times. Each time she blew counted as one trial. Darnell recorded the shape of the bubbles from each trial on a chart like the one shown.

Next, Darnell took a turn and repeated exactly what Alicia had done. Then, to check their results, they each took another turn. They noticed that as a bubble formed, it had the shape of the wand it was made from. But as soon as the bubble left the wand, the bubble became round.

When you do an experiment, you make observations so that you can obtain information called data. You need to write down, or record, this data and then organize it. Graphs and tables are ways to organize data. Analyze the information that you collect by looking for patterns. To see if your results are reliable, repeat the experiment several times.

Shapes of Wands and Bubbles – Alicia

Trial	Bubble Shape from Oval Wand	Bubble Shape from Square Wand
1	round	round
2		
3		
4		
5		
6		

Draw Conclusions

Alicia and Darnell concluded that all bubbles are round. They decided that the shape of the wand doesn't matter. All bubbles look like the wand shape at first. Then they all become round. So Alicia and Darnell concluded that their hypothesis was not correct.

After you have analyzed your data, you should use what you learned to draw a conclusion. A conclusion is a statement that sums up what you learned. The conclusion should be about the hypothesis you made. A hypothesis supported by a lot of evidence may be called a theory.

HOW DO SCIENTISTS BUILD KNOWLEDGE?

The power of scientific thinking becomes evident when scientists share their data, analyses, and results at national and international meetings and in specialized science journals. This communication and teamwork is important because it serves as a way to collect and disseminate scientific findings. Because scientists may draw different conclusions from the same data, it also allows other scientists to challenge, retest, and verify or refute the findings of other researchers.

Scientific Theories

When a hypothesis about natural phenomena is strongly supported by evidence and widely accepted by the scientific community, the hypothesis is called a *theory*. A theory usually explains a broader range of phenomena than does a hypothesis. Also, a theory often includes a demonstrable model of how ideas fit together. New theories can replace older ones as more data is gathered. For example, Copernicus's theory of a heliocentric (Sun-centered) universe replaced Ptolemy's geocentric (Earth-centered) theory when Galileo and others demonstrated conclusively that all objects in the universe did not orbit Earth.

Scientific Laws

Descriptions of natural phenomena are referred to as *scientific laws*. Such descriptions are often mathematical and have great predictive value. Sir Isaac Newton's laws of motion and law of universal gravitation are examples of scientific laws.

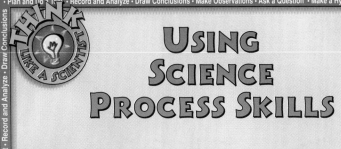

USING SCIENCE PROCESS SKILLS

Observing involves gathering information about the environment through your five senses—seeing, hearing, smelling, touching, and tasting.

Classifying is grouping objects or events according to common properties or characteristics. Often you can classify in more than one way.

Measuring and using numbers involves the ability to make measurements (including time measurements), to make estimates, and to record data.

Communicating involves using words, both speaking and writing, and using actions, graphs, tables, diagrams, and other ways of presenting information.

Inferring means coming to a conclusion based on facts and observations you've made.

Predicting involves stating in advance what you think will happen based on observations and experiences.

Collecting, recording, and interpreting data all involve gathering and understanding information. This skill includes organizing data in tables, graphs, and in other ways. Interpretation includes finding patterns and relationships that lead to new questions and new ideas.

Identifying and controlling variables involves determining the effect of a changing factor, called the variable, in an experiment. To do this, you keep all other factors constant, or unchanging.

Defining operationally means to describe an object, an event, or an idea based on personal observations. An operational definition of a plant might be that it is a green living thing that is attached to soil and that does not move around.

Making a hypothesis is suggesting a possible answer to a question or making an educated guess about why something happens. Your hypothesis should be based on observations and experiences.

Experimenting is testing your hypothesis to collect evidence that supports the hypothesis or shows that it is false.

Making and using models includes designing and making physical models of processes and objects, or making mental models to represent objects and ideas.

HOW CAN SCIENTIFIC THINKING BE APPLIED?

The importance of learning to think scientifically beginning in elementary school cannot be underestimated. Every aspect of home and career in the twenty-first century will require students to apply science process skills. The following activities can be used throughout the year to reinforce the wealth of opportunities *Science DiscoveryWorks* integrates into each Investigation.

Testing Ideas

On a self-stick note or on an index card, have each student write a science question he or she is curious about but can't answer. Have each student describe an observation that prompted the question. On a bulletin board, arrange the notes in the shape of a large question mark. Divide the students into groups. Ask each group to select a question that students in the group think they already know something about or one they

are confident they can answer with a little library research or experimentation. Explain that each group must write a testable hypothesis to answer the question and identify the science process skills they would need to use in answering it. Encourage them to list other questions that occur to them.

What's the Best Money Can Buy?

What brands of supplies should your school purchase? Have students apply science process skills, beginning with observations and questions they have about the supplies they use in school each day, such as crayons, paper, pencils, washroom soap, paper towels and so on. Ask students to choose a product, ask questions about it, and design tests to compare it to other brands. Provide an opportunity to submit the findings to school administrators and board members.

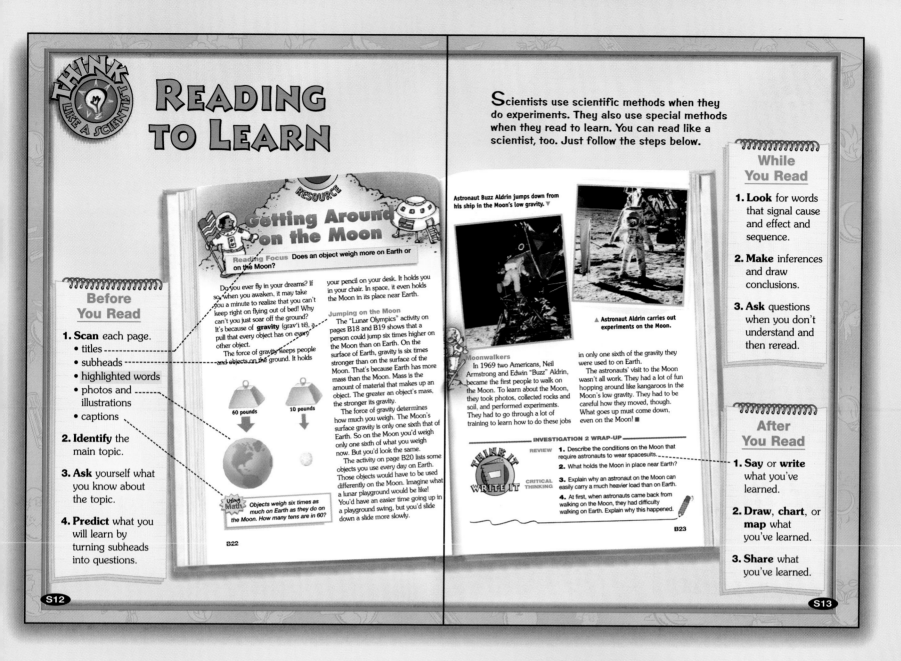

READING TO LEARN

Before Students Read

Discuss each numbered feature with students and explain how each will help them read more effectively.

- Guide students to preview the reading by scanning titles and heads.

- Have students use the Reading Focus question to set a purpose for reading.

- Point out that asking questions helps students engage their interest in the topic.

- Suggest that students look ahead at illustrations and captions to predict what they will find in the reading.

While Students Read

Explain how the numbered strategies can help students while they read.

- Show students how signal words like *first*, *next*, *so*, and *because* identify important relationships such as sequence and cause and effect.

- Help students draw conclusions and make inferences by thinking about what they are reading.

- Have students self-monitor their reading by asking themselves questions as they read.

After Students Read

Encourage students to review what they have read and to assess their understanding by using these strategies.

- Have students restate or write down main ideas and important details to help remember information.

- Show students how using graphic aids such as charts or diagrams help them organize information.

- Point out that sharing what they read helps students summarize what they have read.

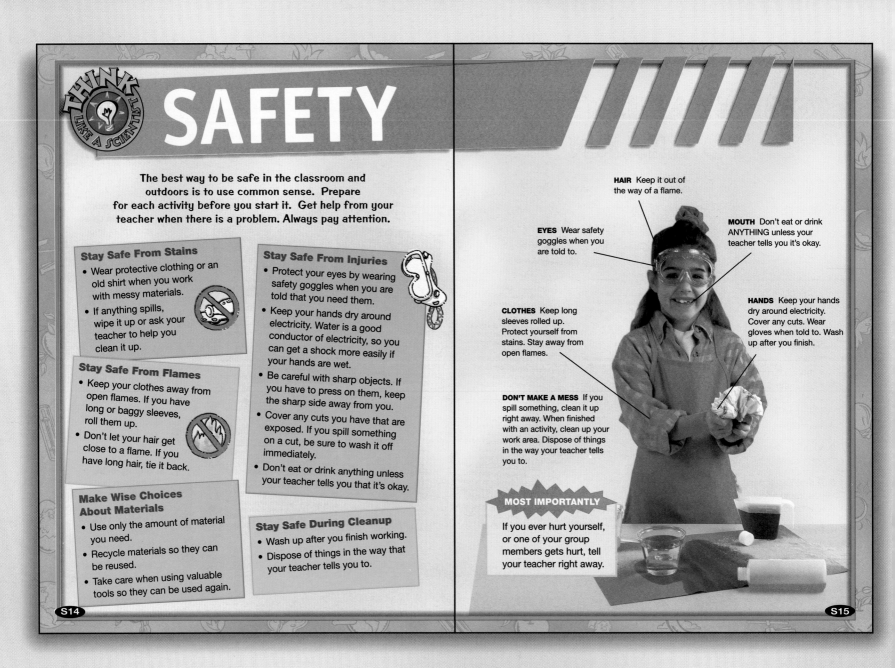

SAFETY

THINK LIKE A SCIENTIST

The best way to be safe in the classroom and outdoors is to use common sense. Prepare for each activity before you start it. Get help from your teacher when there is a problem. Always pay attention.

Stay Safe From Stains
- Wear protective clothing or an old shirt when you work with messy materials.
- If anything spills, wipe it up or ask your teacher to help you clean it up.

Stay Safe From Flames
- Keep your clothes away from open flames. If you have long or baggy sleeves, roll them up.
- Don't let your hair get close to a flame. If you have long hair, tie it back.

Make Wise Choices About Materials
- Use only the amount of material you need.
- Recycle materials so they can be reused.
- Take care when using valuable tools so they can be used again.

Stay Safe From Injuries
- Protect your eyes by wearing safety goggles when you are told that you need them.
- Keep your hands dry around electricity. Water is a good conductor of electricity, so you can get a shock more easily if your hands are wet.
- Be careful with sharp objects. If you have to press on them, keep the sharp side away from you.
- Cover any cuts you have that are exposed. If you spill something on a cut, be sure to wash it off immediately.
- Don't eat or drink anything unless your teacher tells you that it's okay.

Stay Safe During Cleanup
- Wash up after you finish working.
- Dispose of things in the way that your teacher tells you to.

HAIR Keep it out of the way of a flame.

EYES Wear safety goggles when you are told to.

MOUTH Don't eat or drink ANYTHING unless your teacher tells you it's okay.

CLOTHES Keep long sleeves rolled up. Protect yourself from stains. Stay away from open flames.

HANDS Keep your hands dry around electricity. Cover any cuts. Wear gloves when told to. Wash up after you finish.

DON'T MAKE A MESS If you spill something, clean it up right away. When finished with an activity, clean up your work area. Dispose of things in the way your teacher tells you to.

MOST IMPORTANTLY

If you ever hurt yourself, or one of your group members gets hurt, tell your teacher right away.

S14　　S15

SAFETY

In order for students to develop respect for safety, they need to understand exactly what is meant by safe and unsafe behavior and what the rationale is behind safety rules. Through your teaching, students can develop the "safe science" attitudes and skills that are essential both in school and at home.

General Safety Guidelines

- Post an easy-to-read list of safety rules in a prominent place in the classroom. Review it with students on a regular basis.
- Become familiar with the safety procedures that are necessary for each activity before introducing it to your students.
- Discuss specific safety precautions with students before beginning every hands-on science activity.
- Always act as an exemplary model of safe behavior.

- Have students wear protective aprons, goggles, and gloves whenever these items will prevent injury.
- Keep safety equipment, such as extinguishers, readily accessible and know how to use it.
- Prepare students for emergencies by having them practice leaving the classroom quickly and safely.
- Show students how to obtain help in an emergency by using the telephone, an intercom, or other available means of communication.
- Never leave students unattended while they are involved in science activities.
- Provide ample space for activities that require students to move about and handle materials.
- Keep your classroom and all science materials in proper condition. Check their condition regularly.
- Tell students to report injuries to you immediately.

UNIT E

Roles of Living Things

Overview Roles of Living Things examines how living things interact with their environment and with each other to change and adapt to different ecosystems. Through the activities and resources, students discover what living things need in order to survive, different ways that living things get food and protect themselves, and the relationships among organisms in food webs.

Theme An environment is always changing, but in many environments the types of changes have a constant pattern: seasonal changes are quite predictable; changes in light levels tend to follow a progression throughout the year; rain may fall during some parts of the year but not others; nutrients may be available at some times but not others. Over time, living things adapt to take advantage of the constant features of their environment. In order to survive they also must be able to adapt to the sudden changes in the environment.

THE BIG IDEA

To survive, living things must adapt to changes in their environments.

Tracing Major Concepts

 Living things require an environment that meets their needs; living things in an environment are interdependent.

Subconcepts

- Living things need other living things and certain nonliving things in order to survive.

- Living things get their energy in various ways.

- Living things are part of food chains, which are part of food webs.

 Living things have structural and behavioral adaptations that allow them to survive in their environments.

Subconcepts

- Living things vary in their adaptations for getting food, including use of specialized body parts and behaviors, poisonous chemicals, and camouflage.

- Living things vary in their adaptations for protection, including repellent body parts or chemicals, mimicking dangerous creatures, defensive behaviors, and camouflage.

 Living things change their environments and respond to changes in their environments.

Subconcepts

- Living things can alter their environment, and the changes can affect other living things.

- Living things have adaptations that enable them to cope with changes in their environment, such as temperature fluctuations and seasonal changes.

CONTENTS

Roles of Living Things

DiscoveryWorks CORRELATIONS

1. Organisms have basic needs. . . Organisms can survive only in environments in which their needs can be met. . . . *(Ch. 1)*

2. All animals depend on plants. Some animals eat plants for food. Other animals eat animals that eat the plants. *(Ch. 1, Inv. 3)*

3. An organism's patterns of behavior are related to the nature of that organism's environment, . . . When the environment changes, some plants and animals survive and reproduce, and others die or move to new locations. *(Ch. 3)*

4. Resources are things that we get from the . . . environment to meet the needs and wants of a population. *(Ch. 1, Inv. 1)*

5. Environments are the . . . factors that affect . . . a population's ability to survive and their quality of life. *(Ch. 1, Inv. 1)*

6. Changes in environments can be natural or influenced by humans. Some changes are good, some are bad, and some are neither good nor bad. . . . *(Ch. 1, Inv. 3; Ch. 3, Inv. 1)*

1. A great variety of . . . living things can be sorted into groups . . . *(Ch. 1)*

2. For any particular environment, some kinds of plants and animals survive well, some survive less well, and some cannot survive at all. *(Ch. 1, Inv. 1;*

Ch. 2; Ch. 3)*

3. Insects and various other organisms depend on dead plant and animal material for food. *(Ch. 1, Inv. 2)*

4. Changes in an organism's habitat are sometimes beneficial to it and sometimes harmful. *(Ch. 3, Inv. 1)*

5. Almost all kinds of animals' food can be traced back to plants. *(Ch. 1, Inv. 3)*

6. Some source of "energy" is needed for all organisms to . . . *(Ch. 1, Inv. 1 and 2)*

7. The damage to crops . . . can be reduced by using poisons, but their use may harm other plants. . . . *(Ch. 1, Inv. 3)*

NSES Standards are based on *National Science Education Standards* (© 1996) published by The National Research Council.
Project 2061 Benchmarks are based on *Benchmarks for Science Literacy* (© 1993) published by The American Association for the Advancement of Science.

CURRICULUM INTEGRATION

An integrated approach to the teaching of science will help students understand how science connects to other school subjects as well as to technology and to literature. The chart below indicates where to find the activities in this unit that connect to other disciplines.

THE SCIENCES

- Earth Science, page E18
- Earth Science, page E49
- Earth Science, page E52
- Earth Science, page E65

LITERATURE

- Reading, page E29
- *One Small Square: African Savanna,* page E31
- Aesop's Fables, page E48
- *Piranhas and Other Wonders of the Jungle,* pages E52, E65
- Desert Study, page E70

MATH

- Graphing, page E12
- Measuring, page E42
- Round-Trip Migration, page E79

WRITING

- Presentations, page E16
- Listing Game, page E17
- Creative Writing, page E20
- Making a Menu, page E26
- Letter Writing, page E28
- Flow Charts, page E31
- Using Verbs, page E41
- About Dogs, page E53

CONNECTING SCIENCE TO

SCIENCE AROUND THE WORLD

- Keeping Cool, page E10
- Different Foods, page E19
- Saving Nature, page E33
- Medicine Study, page E54
- Designing, page E71

SOCIAL STUDIES

- Eels and Maps, page E11
- Florida Everglades, page E30
- Researching, page E43
- Using Maps, page E62
- Identifying, page E66
- Migration, page E75

TECHNOLOGY & SOCIETY

- Factory Waste, page E23
- Interviewing, page E32
- Adaptation, page E40
- Infections, page E51
- Global Warming, page E72

THE ARTS

- Draw a Cartoon, page E27
- Painting, page E50
- Making Models, page E63
- Illustrating, page E74

Animals' Colors in Nature

by Dr. Linda Cronin-Jones

Dr. Linda Cronin-Jones has been an associate professor of science and environmental education at the University of Florida at Gainesville since 1986. She teaches courses in science curriculum evaluation, environmental education, and science education.

THE ADVERTISERS

Nature's palette of colors and patterns provides a constant source of delight and inspiration. The many colors found in Earth's animals also serve a valuable purpose: they help animals survive.

Brightly-colored birds, such as birds of paradise, use coloration to attract a mate. Many amphibians, insects, and fish, such as poison arrow frogs, yellow jacket hornets, and venomous lionfish, use their bright colors to warn potential predators of poisoning, a painful sting, or just a very bad taste. Other animals, such as the white-tailed deer, use body coloration to warn of impending danger.

THE CONCEALERS

Many animals, both predator and prey, possess colors and patterns that help them blend in with their surroundings. For example, the snowshoe and arctic hares go from brown to white as fall changes to winter; they do the reverse as spring changes to summer. These seasonal changes preserve their camouflage.

Many water dwellers, such as sharks, dolphins, and sea turtles, possess a form of coloration called countershading. These animals are usually dark on top and light on the underside. When viewed from above, they blend in with the dark color of the water below. When seen from below, they blend in with the sunlit water above.

THE CONFUSERS

Some animals possess color patterns, called disruptive coloration, that confuse potential predators or prey. For example, the copperband butterflyfish has a large, black eyespot near its tail, which many predators mistake for an eye. Predators get confused when it swims off in the direction opposite to that which they expected. The colors and patterns of coral reef fish, such as grouper and clown anemone fish, make it difficult for predators to see the outline of their preys' bodies. Predators, such as cuttle fish, change colors rapidly to dazzle and distract their prey, making them easier to capture.

THE MIMICS

Some animals mimic the colorations of others. Batesian mimicry involves a harmful animal and a harmless animal. For example, the tender, juicy viceroy butterfly's colors mimic the noxious-tasting monarch butterfly, and the harmless beefly looks like a stinging bee. Predators tend to avoid all mimics just to be safe.

◀ The imperial moth (*far left*) and the leaf mantid (*near left*) are two examples of concealers.

TIPS FROM Teachers

Try This!

Students can enact a simple food chain by assuming the roles of organisms. Give each student a sign with the name of an organism. Have students form chains by holding hands with organisms they would eat and ones that would eat them. The group can then dramatize the impact on the entire food chain of increasing or decreasing the number of any one kind of organism.

Sr. Sharon Kassing
St. Louis, Missouri

Try This!

Give each student some construction paper, crayons, and a pair of scissors. Have them decorate the paper to blend in with some object in the classroom. Challenge students from another class to find and collect as many of the camouflaged drawings as they can in a given time period.

Shirley Hall
Philadelphia,
Pennsylvania

Try This!

Have students go outside to a defined area of the schoolyard. Let them observe and record all evidence of life they find there—for example, animal droppings and feathers, tree bark, and leaves. Have them name all the animals and plants for which they find evidence. When they have a complete list, ask them to describe how the area serves as a home for animals and plants. Have them describe how the living things they found might interact and depend on each other.

Patricia Ramsey
Williamsburg,
Virginia

SKILLS FOR SCIENTIFIC LITERACY

Science **DiscoveryWorks** helps students develop scientific literacy by providing activities and resources that challenge students to use process skills, critical thinking skills, and scientific reasoning skills. Students develop process skills as they ask questions and investigate to discover the answers. They develop critical thinking skills and scientific reasoning skills as they respond to thought-provoking questions about their investigations and in on-going assessment.

Science Process Skills

Science process skills provide a framework in which ideas can be conceptualized, tested, and evaluated. The processes listed here are developed through a wide range of hands-on experiences.

Activities	Page	Observing	Classifying	Measuring/ Using Numbers	Communicating	Inferring	Predicting	Collecting, Recording, and Interpreting Data	Identifying and Controlling Variables	Defining Operationally	Making Hypotheses	Experimenting	Making and Using Models
Needs of Plants	E6	•		•		•	•	•	•	•			
A Pill Bug's Home	E8	•				•	•	•	•	•		•	
Meat and Potatoes	E14		•			•	•						
A Menu for Molds	E15	•				•	•	•	•			•	
Making a Food-Chain Mobile	E22		•		•	•				•			•
More Links in the Food Chain	E24					•				•	•		•
The Right Beak for the Job	E38	•		•		•	•	•			•		•
Blending In	E46				•	•	•				•		•
My Neighborhood Keeps Changing!	E60	•	•			•	•		•			•	
Keeping Heat In	E68			•			•	•		•		•	•	•

Critical Thinking Skills

Critical thinking skills are embedded in the questioning strategies throughout the program. The chart below summarizes the processes assessed in the Think It/Write It sections that end each investigation.

Process	Description	E13	E21	E34	E45	E56	E67	E76
Analyzing	Studying something to identify constituent elements or relationships among elements	●	●	●	●	●		●
Synthesizing	Using deductive reasoning to pull together key elements	●	●				●	●
Evaluating	Reviewing and responding critically to materials, procedures, or ideas and judging them by purposes, standards, or other criteria		●	●	●		●	●
Applying	Using ideas, processes, or skills in new situations	●		●			●	●
Generating Ideas	Expressing thoughts that reveal originality, speculation, imagination, a personal perspective, flexibility in thinking, invention, or creativity	●				●	●	
Expressing Ideas	Presenting ideas clearly and in logical order, while using language that is appropriate for the audience and occasion		●	●	●	●	●	●
Solving Problems	Using critical thinking processes to find solutions to a problem	●	●					

Scientific Reasoning Skills

Scientific reasoning skills are developed and reinforced through the science process skills and critical thinking skills.

Reasoning Skill	Description
Longing to Know and Understand	The desire to probe, find information, and seek explanations
Questioning of Scientific Assumptions	The tendency to hold open for further verification of presented assumptions, encounters, and ideas
Searching for Data and Its Meaning	The propensity to collect information and to analyze it in context
Demand for Verification	The inclination to repeat and replicate findings and studies
Respect for Logic	The inclination to move from assumptions to testing and data collection to conclusions
Consideration of Premises	The tendency to put into context the reason for a particular point of view
Consideration of Consequences	The tendency to put into perspective the results of a particular point of view
Respect for Historical Contributions	The inclination to understand and learn from the contributions of earlier ideas, studies, events, and so on

ONGOING ASSESSMENT

Houghton Mifflin Science DiscoveryWorks provides a variety of ongoing assessment tools to help you monitor student growth.

 ## Written Reviews and Tests

Written reviews and tests throughout the program help assess student learning.

In the Student Edition
- Analyze & Conclude questions at end of each Activity
- Think It/Write It questions at end of each Investigation
- Reflect & Evaluate questions at end of each chapter

In the Teacher Resource Book
- Investigation Reviews
- Chapter Tests/Unit Tests
- Chapter and Unit Tests in standardized test format

 ## Performance Assessment

Performance Assessment tasks allow students to demonstrate their learning through hands-on activities.

In the Teaching Guide Performance tasks appear at end of specific investigations and end of each chapter.

In the Teacher Resource Book A Unit Performance Task, with accompanying rubric, appears in each unit.

 ## Portfolio Assessment

Portfolios of student work can be used to holistically assess student progress. Portfolio support material is provided in the Ongoing Assessment section of the TRB.

In the Student Edition A portfolio suggestion appears at end of chapter.

In the Teaching Guide Portfolio tasks appear at end of specific investigations.

Chapter 1
Assessment Options

Investigation 1 Review

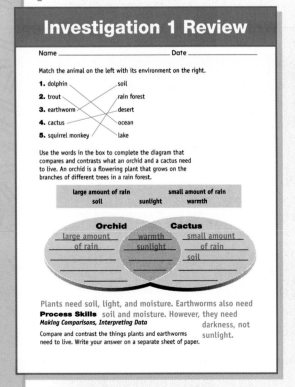

Ongoing Assessment, TRB p. 107

Investigation 2 Review

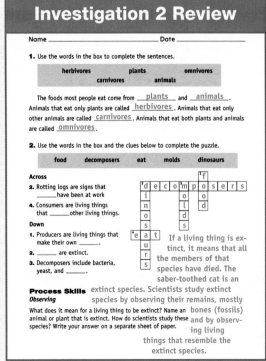

Ongoing Assessment, TRB p. 108

Investigation 3 Review

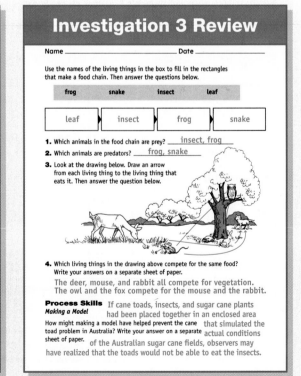

Ongoing Assessment, TRB p. 109

Chapter Test

Name _____ Date _____

Check What You Know Each item is worth 6 points.

For questions 1–4, circle the letter of the word or words that best complete each sentence.

1. The three basic things you need to live are food, water, and ____.
   a. soil   **b.** the ocean   **c.** trees   **(d.)** air

2. One kind of producer is a ____.
   (a.) plant   **b.** fish   **c.** spider   **d.** cricket

3. Food chains overlap to form ____.
   a. environments   **b.** communities   **(c.)** food webs   **d.** food circles

4. An animal that eats only plants is a(n) ____.
   a. omnivore   **b.** producer   **c.** carnivore   **(d.)** herbivore

Word Power Each item is worth 7 points.

Use the words in the box to complete each sentence.

consumer	decomposer	habitat
food chain		extinction

5. A place where a living thing lives is its ___habitat___.

6. ___Extinction___ is the dying out of all living things of a certain kind.

7. A living thing that eats other living things is a ___consumer___.

8. A living thing that eats dead organisms is a ___decomposer___.

9. A ___food chain___ is the path energy takes as one living thing eats another.

Ongoing Assessment, TRB p. 110

Chapter Test

Name _____ Date _____

Problem Solving Each item is worth 9 points.

10. Draw a line from the animal to the environment it would live best in.

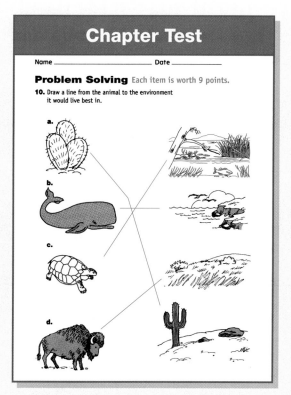

Ongoing Assessment, TRB p. 111

Pressed for Time Test

Name _____ Date _____

Check What You Know Each item is worth 10 points.

For questions 1–5, circle the letter of the correct answer.

1. The three basic things you need to live are food, water, and ____.
   a. soil   **b.** the ocean   **c.** trees   **(d.)** air

2. Everything that surrounds and affects a living thing is its ____.
   (a.) environment   **b.** food chain   **c.** food web   **d.** habitat

3. Food chains overlap to form ____.
   a. environments   **b.** communities   **c.** food circles   **(d.)** food webs

4. A ____ is a living thing that eats other living things.
   a. decomposer   **(b.)** consumer   **c.** producer   **d.** mushroom

5. A place where an animal or plant lives is its ____.
   (a.) habitat   **b.** wetland   **c.** environment   **d.** ocean

Word Power Each item is worth 10 points.

Use the words in the box to complete each sentence.

predator	prey	omnivore	herbivore	carnivore

The foods that most people eat come from plants and animals. An animal that eats only plants is called a(n) ___herbivore___. An animal that eats only other animals is called a(n) ___carnivore___. Some animals, such as the brown bear, eat both plants and animals. An animal that eats both plants and animals is called a(n) ___omnivore___. When a brown bear eats a fish, the bear is the ___predator___ and the fish is the ___prey___.

Ongoing Assessment, TRB p. 112

Chapter 2
Assessment Options

Investigation 1 Review

Name _____ Date _____

Draw a line from the adaptation on the left to the phrase on the right that best describes how it helps the animal.

1. chameleon's eyes   catch and eat large fish

2. hummingbird's long beak and tongue   watch for predator and prey at same time

3. bear's claws and teeth   paralyze and kill prey

4. snake's poison fangs   sip nectar from flower

Use the clues below to unscramble the letters of each word.

5. I am a parrot. I use my strong ____ to crack nuts.
   K B E A   ___BEAK___

6. I am a sea otter. I get some of my food by using a rock as a ____.
   O L O T   ___TOOL___

7. I am a leopard. I can catch a gazelle by behaving in a certain way. I ____, or secretly follow and sneak up on, my prey.
   T L K S A   ___STALK___

8. Animals in nature must work hard to get food. Their task is made easier by their ____.
   P T T O N A D S A I A   ___ADAPTATIONS___

Lower light levels at night make it more difficult to see. While night hunters usually have vision that is adapted to the dark, a sharp sense of hearing helps them locate prey before they can see it.

Process Skills
Hypothesizing

Hypothesize why owls, bats, and other night hunters have highly developed senses of hearing. Write your hypothesis on a separate sheet of paper.

Ongoing Assessment, TRB p. 113

Investigation 2 Review

Name _____ Date _____

Circle the word or words that best complete each sentence.

1. The adaptations of a rose that protect it are found on the ____.
    leaves   (stems)   flowers

2. The adaptation of a marigold plant that protects it is its ____.
    (bitter taste)   strong smell   dull color

3. When the puffer fish blows itself up into a spine-covered ball, its ____ helps to protect it.
    smell   color   (size)

4. A brown moth lands on the bark of a tree. The moth blends with the bark and seems to disappear because of the moth's ____.
    size   shape   (color)

5. Match the picture with the word or phrase that describes the adaptation.

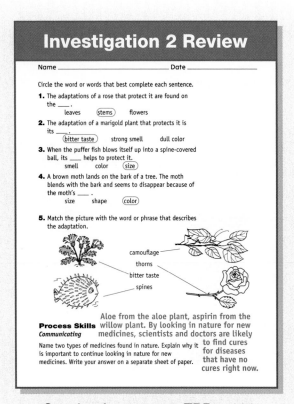

    camouflage
    thorns
    bitter taste
    spines

Process Skills
Communicating

Name two types of medicines found in nature. Explain why it is important to continue looking in nature for new medicines. Write your answer on a separate sheet of paper.

Aloe from the aloe plant, aspirin from the willow plant. By looking in nature for new medicines, scientists and doctors are likely to find cures for diseases that have no cures right now.

Ongoing Assessment, TRB p. 114

Chapter Test

Name _____ Date _____

Check What You Know Each item is worth 6 points.

For questions 1–4, circle the letter of the answer that best completes each sentence.

1. One animal that can be camouflaged on the forest floor is a ____.
    (a.) fawn   c. coral snake
    b. yellow jacket   d. blue bird

2. Some animals use tools from the environment to help them gather food. One such animal is the ____.
    a. woodpecker   c. dog
    b. owl   (d.) chimpanzee

3. A(n) ____ is an animal that protects itself by tricking predators into thinking it is dead.
    a. spider   c. coral snake
    (b.) opossum   d. grasshopper

4. Many kinds of medicines are made from ____.
    a. bird feathers   c. snake blood
    (b.) plants   d. insects

Word Power Each item is worth 7 points.

Write the letter of the term that best matches the definition.

 _c_ **5.** the ability to blend in with the colors of one's surroundings   **a.** adaptation

 _d_ **6.** substance that provides a living thing with the materials needed for growth   **b.** behavior

 _a_ **7.** behavior or part of a living thing that helps it survive in a certain environment   **c.** camouflage

 _e_ **8.** a living thing that lives on or in another living thing   **d.** nutrient

 _b_ **9.** the way a living thing typically acts in a certain situation   **e.** parasite

Ongoing Assessment, TRB p. 115

Chapter Test

Name _____ Date _____

Problem Solving Each item is worth 10 points.

10. Draw a circle around the adaptations shown. Explain your answers on the lines provided.

Accept any answers that students can justify.

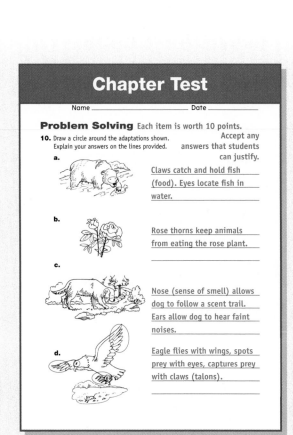

a. Claws catch and hold fish (food). Eyes locate fish in water.

b. Rose thorns keep animals from eating the rose plant.

c. Nose (sense of smell) allows dog to follow a scent trail. Ears allow dog to hear faint noises.

d. Eagle flies with wings, spots prey with eyes, captures prey with claws (talons).

Ongoing Assessment, TRB p. 116

Pressed for Time Test

Name _____ Date _____

Check What You Know Each item is worth 10 points.

For questions 1–5, circle the letter of the correct answer.

1. The elephant allows the tickbird to perch on its back because the tickbird ____.
    a. helps camouflage the elephant   (**c.**) eats annoying insects
    b. scares away predators   **d.** sings softly

2. A(n) ____ of the praying mantis is to use its front legs to trap insects.
    a. tool   (**b.**) adaptation   **c.** camouflage   **d.** nutrient

3. One animal that can be hidden on the forest floor is a ____.
    (**a.**) fawn   **b.** yellow jacket   **c.** coral snake   **d.** bluebird

4. Opossums "play dead" so that other animals won't ____ them.
    a. see   (**b.**) eat   **c.** play with   **d.** hide from

5. The Venus' flytrap is a special plant that gets ____ from insects.
    a. pollinated   **b.** camouflage   **c.** sick   (**d.**) nutrients

Word Power Each item is worth 10 points.

Write the letter of the term that best matches the definition.

 _b_ **6.** the ability to blend in with the colors of one's surroundings   **a.** adaptation

 _e_ **7.** substance that provides a living thing with the materials needed for growth   **b.** camouflage

 _a_ **8.** behavior or part of a living thing that helps it survive in a certain environment   **c.** parasite

 _c_ **9.** a living thing that lives on or in other living things   **d.** behavior

 _d_ **10.** the way a living thing typically acts in a certain situation   **e.** nutrient

Ongoing Assessment, TRB p. 117

Investigation 1 Review

Name _____ Date _____

Look at the picture. Then answer the questions below.

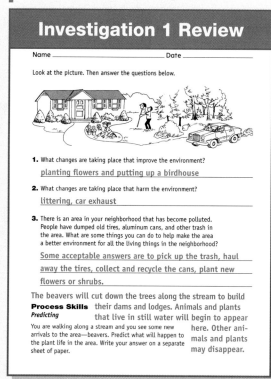

1. What changes are taking place that improve the environment?

planting flowers and putting up a birdhouse

2. What changes are taking place that harm the environment?

littering, car exhaust

3. There is an area in your neighborhood that has become polluted. People have dumped old tires, aluminum cans, and other trash in the area. What are some things you can do to help make the area a better environment for all the living things in the neighborhood?

Some acceptable answers are to pick up the trash, haul
away the tires, collect and recycle the cans, plant new
flowers or shrubs.

Process Skills
Predicting

The beavers will cut down the trees along the stream to build their dams and lodges. Animals and plants that live in still water will begin to appear here. Other animals and plants may disappear.

You are walking along a stream and you see some new arrivals to the area—beavers. Predict what will happen to the plant life in the area. Write your answer on a separate sheet of paper.

Ongoing Assessment, TRB p. 118

Investigation 2 Review

Name _____ Date _____

1. Circle the sentence about the desert animals that is **not** true.

a. Stilt beetles keep cool by tiptoeing across the hot sand.

b. Many desert animals sweat, which keeps them cool.

c. A kangaroo rat may go its entire life without drinking water.

d. The white wax on desert beetles reflects the sun and keeps in moisture.

2. Animals and plants have many different ways to deal with harsh environments or changes in their environments. Match the animal or plant on the left with its adaptation on the right. Then answer the question below.

d	Arctic tern	**a.** hibernates in winter
c	kangaroo rat	**b.** becomes dormant in winter
e	cactus	**c.** stays in its cool burrow during the day
a	woodchuck	**d.** migrates to a warmer climate
b	oak tree	**e.** stores water in its thick stems

3. What special adaptation do you have to help you deal with hot summer weather?

I perspire, or sweat. When the drops of sweat dry, or
evaporate, my body becomes cooler.

Process Skills
Making a Model

What did making a model of a bird tell you about how a bird protects itself from the cold?

A bird's feathers hold in body heat and protect it from
the cold.

Ongoing Assessment, TRB p. 119

Chapter Test

Name _____ Date _____

Check What You Know Each item is worth 8 points.

For questions 1–4, circle the letter of the word or words that best complete each sentence.

1. People make changes that do not harm the environment when they ____.

a. build large buildings   **c.** drain wetlands

b. plant trees and gardens   **d.** build skyscrapers

2. A beaver changes the environment by ____.

a. draining ponds   **c.** building mounds

b. digging up the soil   **d.** damming up streams

3. One way living things have become adapted to the desert environment is by being able to ____.

a. conserve water   **c.** perspire, or sweat

b. migrate   **d.** grow trees

4. A(n) ____ is an animal that hibernates during the long, cold winter.

a. Arctic tern   **c.** woodchuck

b. kangaroo rat   **d.** deer

Word Power Each item is worth 7 points.

Write the letter of the term that best matches the definition.

d	**5.**	an environment made up of many grasses that is home to the American bison, or buffalo	**a.** desert
e	**6.**	land that is soaked with water and is home to many birds, frogs, and other animals	**b.** hibernation
b	**7.**	a deep sleep during winter for certain animals	**c.** migrate
a	**8.**	an environment that has little water and is usually hot during the day	**d.** prairie
c	**9.**	to move to a new area when the seasons change	**e.** wetland

Ongoing Assessment, TRB p. 120

Chapter Test

Name _____ Date _____

Problem Solving Each item is worth 15 points.

The Hoh Rain Forest is located in the state of Washington. The evergreen trees growing there are hundreds of years old and reach hundreds of meters into the sky. Some junglelike plants grow on the forest floor. Mosses hang from the branches and cover the tree trunks. Many different kinds of birds fly from branch to branch. Elk, black bears, mountain lions, and other animals roam throughout the forest.

10. Explain how cutting down all the trees would change the environment.

Cutting down all the trees would drastically alter the
environment. Habitats would be destroyed, forcing
forest animals to move or die. Accept all reasonable
answers.

11. Make a hypothesis as to what might happen if only selected trees were cut. [HINT: Think about any positive changes that might occur.]

Removing selected trees would make open areas
in the forest. These could stimulate growth of
underbrush, providing new areas of shelter and food
for living things. Accept all reasonable answers.

Ongoing Assessment, TRB p. 121

Pressed for Time Test

Name _____ Date _____

Check What You Know   Each item is worth 10 points.

For questions 1–5, circle the letter of the correct answer.

1. People make changes that do not harm the environment when they _____ .
- **a.** dig for fossil fuels
- **c.** drain wetlands
- **(b.)** plant trees and gardens
- **d.** build skyscrapers

2. A beaver changes the environment by _____ .
- **a.** swimming in ponds
- **c.** building mounds
- **b.** digging up the soil
- **(d.)** damming up streams

3. Some living things have adapted to the desert by being able to _____ .
- **(a.)** conserve water
- **c.** perspire, or sweat
- **b.** migrate
- **d.** grow trees

4. A woodchuck is an animal that _____ during the long, cold winter.
- **(a.)** hibernates
- **c.** eats
- **b.** migrates
- **d.** changes the environment

5. An animal's hibernation is like a plant's _____ .
- **a.** pollination
- **c.** migration
- **b.** blooming
- **(d.)** dormancy

Word Power   Each item is worth 10 points.

Write the letter of the term that best matches the definition.

_e_ **6.** land that is soaked with water and is home to many birds, frogs, and other animals

_c_ **7.** go into a deep sleep in the winter

_a_ **8.** an environment that has little water and is usually hot during the day

_b_ **9.** move to a new area when seasons change

_d_ **10.** place where living and nonliving things interact

- **a.** desert
- **b.** migrate
- **c.** hibernate
- **d.** ecosystem
- **e.** wetland

Ongoing Assessment, TRB p. 122

Unit Test

Name _____ Date _____

Check What You Know   Each item is worth 5 points.

For questions 1–9, circle the letter of the word or words that best complete each sentence.

1. A lion eats other animals. A lion is a(n) _____.
- **a.** decomposer
- **b.** producer
- **c.** herbivore
- **(d.)** carnivore

2. A giraffe eats only plants. A giraffe is a(n) _____.
- **a.** decomposer
- **(b.)** herbivore
- **c.** producer
- **d.** omnivore

3. A lizard eats a cricket. The cricket is, in this case, the _____.
- **(a.)** prey
- **b.** predator
- **c.** consumer
- **d.** producer

4. Some animals use tools to gather or eat food. One such animal is a _____.
- **(a.)** sea otter
- **b.** dog
- **c.** rattlesnake
- **d.** grasshopper

5. Some plants protect themselves by releasing irritating chemicals. Others protect themselves with _____.
- **a.** movement
- **b.** parasites
- **(c.)** thorns
- **d.** hibernation

6. One animal that greatly changes its environment is a _____.
- **a.** katydid
- **b.** kangaroo rat
- **c.** buffalo
- **(d.)** beaver

7. A fawn is protected by its ability to keep very still and by _____.
- **a.** looking like another animal
- **(b.)** camouflage
- **c.** tricking predators into thinking it is dead
- **d.** smelling sweet

Ongoing Assessment, TRB p. 127

Unit Test

Name _____ Date _____

8. An adaptation that a living thing in the desert does **not** have is _____ .
- **(a.)** sweating.
- **c.** spines instead of large leaves.
- **b.** waxy leaves.
- **d.** sleeping during the day.

9. A robin is a bird that eats worms. What does the robin do when the weather gets cold and the worms go very deep into the ground?
- **a.** The robin hibernates.
- **c.** The robin eats toads.
- **(b.)** The robin migrates.
- **d.** The robin gathers acorns.

10. Use the picture to make a food chain. Write the names of the living things in the food chain in the boxes below. The first one has been done for you.

| leaf | ▶ | caterpillar | ▶ | bird | ▶ | cat |

Ongoing Assessment, TRB p. 128

Unit Test

Name _____ Date _____

11. Look at the picture of the chameleon. List two adaptations it has to help it survive or to protect itself.

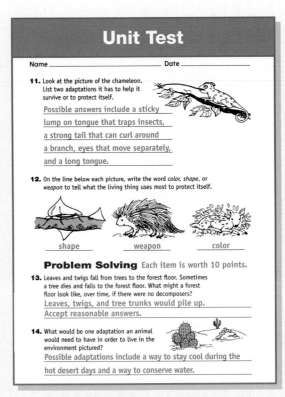

Possible answers include a sticky lump on tongue that traps insects, a strong tail that can curl around a branch, eyes that move separately, and a long tongue.

12. On the line below each picture, write the word *color, shape,* or *weapon* to tell what the living thing uses most to protect itself.

shape   weapon   color

Problem Solving   Each item is worth 10 points.

13. Leaves and twigs fall from trees to the forest floor. Sometimes a tree dies and falls to the forest floor. What might a forest floor look like, over time, if there were no decomposers?

Leaves, twigs, and tree trunks would pile up. Accept reasonable answers.

14. What would be one adaptation an animal would need to have in order to live in the environment pictured?

Possible adaptations include a way to stay cool during the hot desert days and a way to conserve water.

Ongoing Assessment, TRB p. 129

Unit Test

Name _____ Date _____

15. The picture shows one way that people can change the environment. What will happen to the plants and animals that live here? List one thing about this scene that might be done differently to help save the environment.

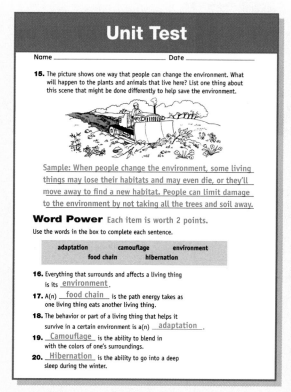

Sample: When people change the environment, some living things may lose their habitats and may even die, or they'll move away to find a new habitat. People can limit damage to the environment by not taking all the trees and soil away.

Word Power Each item is worth 2 points.

Use the words in the box to complete each sentence.

adaptation	camouflage	environment
	food chain	hibernation

16. Everything that surrounds and affects a living thing is its _environment_.

17. A(n) _food chain_ is the path energy takes as one living thing eats another living thing.

18. The behavior or part of a living thing that helps it survive in a certain environment is a(n) _adaptation_.

19. _Camouflage_ is the ability to blend in with the colors of one's surroundings.

20. _Hibernation_ is the ability to go into a deep sleep during the winter.

Ongoing Assessment, TRB p. 130

Pressed for Time Test

Name _____ Date _____

Check What You Know Each item is worth 5 points.

For questions 1–7, circle the letter of the correct answer.

1. A lion eats other animals. A lion is a(n) _____.
   a. decomposer **b.** producer **c.** herbivore **d.** carnivore ⟵

2. A lizard eats a cricket. The cricket is, in this case, the _____.
   a. prey ⟵ **b.** predator **c.** consumer **d.** producer

3. One animal that uses tools to eat food is a _____.
   a. dog **b.** sea otter ⟵ **c.** rattlesnake **d.** horse

4. Some plants protect themselves with _____.
   a. movement **b.** hibernation **c.** thorns ⟵ **d.** parasites

5. The _____ is an animal that greatly changes its environment.
   a. beaver ⟵ **b.** kangaroo rat **c.** buffalo **d.** katydid

6. Animals that blend in with their surroundings use _____ to hide.
   a. migration **b.** hibernation **c.** camouflage ⟵ **d.** poison

7. A giraffe eats only plants. A giraffe is a(n) _____.
   a. decomposer **b.** herbivore ⟵ **c.** producer **d.** omnivore

For questions 8–13, fill in the blank with the correct word or phrase.

8. Wetlands and deserts have very different amounts of ___water___.

9. Trout live in fresh water. Whales live in ___salt___ water.

10. Bacteria, molds, and mushrooms are all ___decomposers___.

11. Most food chains begin with ___plants___, which are also called producers.

12. Birds have different-shaped ___beaks___ so they can catch food. Another possible answer is claws

13. The ___bitter___ taste of marigolds keeps rabbits from eating them.

Ongoing Assessment, TRB p. 131

Pressed for Time Test

Name _____ Date _____

Word Power Each item is worth 5 points.

Use the words in the box to complete each sentence.

hibernation	parasite	food chain	environment	producer

14. A(n) _environment_ is everything that surrounds and affects a living thing.

15. A living thing that can make its own food is a(n) _producer_.

16. A ground squirrel's heart rate and breathing slow down during _hibernation_.

17. The path energy takes as one living thing eats another living thing is called a(n) _food chain_.

18. A tick is a(n) _parasite_ that gathers nutrients from the blood of another animal.

Problem Solving Each item is worth 5 points.

19. A robin is a bird that can fly long distances. Robins eat worms. In the winter, worms go very deep into the ground. What do you think a robin does when winter arrives and snow covers the ground? Explain your answer.

Robins migrate to warmer areas where they can find worms or other types of food. A robin does not have a long beak or any tool to help it dig into the ground, so it must travel to another area where food is plentiful.

20. Leaves and twigs fall from trees to the forest floor. Sometimes a tree dies and falls to the forest floor. What might a forest floor look like, over time, if there were no decomposers?

Accept reasonable answers. A sample answer is that leaves, twigs, and tree trunks would pile up.

Ongoing Assessment, TRB p. 132

Additional Unit Support Material

Student Recording Sheets
See *Science Notebook*, TRB pp. 25–70.

Support Masters for Unit Activities
See Teacher Resource Book pp. 14–15.

Support Masters for Unit Project
See Teacher Resource Book pp. 16–22.

Letters and Activities to send home
See Teacher Resource Book pp. 2–6.

Support Masters for vocabulary development
See Reading Support Book.

Reading Transparencies for concept development
See Reading Support Transparencies.

Chapter and Unit Tests in Standardized Test Format
See Standardized Test Practice, TRB pp. 145–161.

Creating a Tropical Rain Forest Mural

Students research the importance of rain forest plants and animals and the impact of people on rain forests.

Getting Ready

 Groups of 4 to 6 students

For each project link, have each group choose a different topic to research. Then each group can share their findings with the class.

Materials

For Research

- Reference books

For Mural Construction

- Construction paper, scrap paper, poster board, scissors, tape, paste, string, markers, watercolors, crayons or colored pencils

Other Materials

- Unit Project Masters 1–7, TRB pp. 16–22
- *Science Notebook,* TRB pp. 42, 55, 66

Plan Ahead

Decide where the mural should be constructed. You may wish to cover a wall, or a section of a wall, with blank poster board and have students use this as the background for their mural.

Building the Project

Through Project Links

 Chapter 1, p. E25 Each group may choose a different rain forest layer to research and design for the mural. Have groups share their research findings with the class. Encourage students to find creative ways to decorate the rain forest mural.

 Chapter 2, p. E47 Each group may be responsible for researching a different type of animal. Mammals, insects, amphibians, birds, fish, and reptiles should all be included. Students can hide camouflaged animals in the rain forest mural and challenge others to find them.

Assessing Student Progress: The mural should reflect the large variety of plant and animal life that can be found in a tropical rain forest.

 Chapter 3, p. E73 One group can research resources that are found in rain forests. Another group can research why the rain forests are being cut down. A third group may consider what the consequences will be if the destruction of rain forests does not stop. Another group may find out ways kids can help save the rain forests. After sharing their ideas, the groups can make posters displaying what they have learned.

Assessing Student Progress: Students should understand the value and importance of protecting tropical rain forests.

TechnologyLink

You can have students visit our Web site at **www.eduplace.com** to access additional content-related resources, locate agencies that can help with the Unit Projects, and link to experts. You can download Unit Project Masters and obtain a scoring rubric. Classes can also share the results of their projects on-line.

Wrapping Up the Project

Rain Forest Celebration Day

Allow students to have as much input as possible into the planning of Rain Forest Celebration Day. Ask students to make invitations, which could be sent to parents and to other classes. Students can decide how to display the posters and the mural. They may have other ideas on how to transform the classroom into a tropical rain forest. If refreshments will be served, the class can brainstorm for appropriate rain forest foods, such as fruit juices, mangoes, pineapples, coconuts, brazil nuts, and rain forest crunch candy or cereal.

When visitors arrive, each group could give presentations explaining different aspects of the rain forests. One group may talk about the camouflage of animals, while another might focus on the different layers of the rain forests.

People to Contact

In Person

- Contact an ecologist to describe to the class the relationship among organisms and between organisms and the environment.

By Mail

- **Earth Ecology Foundation,** 612 N. 2nd Street, Fresno, CA 93702

- **Rainforest Alliance,** 270 Lafayette Street, Suite 512, New York, NY 10012

BILL NYE
the Science Guy

There's no one better than scientist-comic-author-former engineer Bill Nye to show students how "Science Rules!"

Food Web

Use this episode with Chapter 1.

What's eating you? Everything, if you're a plant. In this episode, Bill constructs a "Food-Glorious-Food Web" out of string to show how plants are more than just chicken feed when it comes to the components of his chicken sandwich. What's more, plants make our oxygen, so Bill goes "deep" to explain that most plants are underwater. As he "flippers" through the aisles, where most of us hunt and gather our food, he makes connections to the food pyramid and shows how, if you're hungry, plants are at the bottom of it.

Video Features

Nifty Home Experiment: Have Sunlight, Will Grow To prove that plants need light to grow, put one onion in a glass of water on a windowsill and another in a dark closet. Wait a few days, then observe.

Consider the Following In a discussion of sugar, oxygen, and carbon dioxide, Bill explains why we wouldn't be breathing in or out if it weren't for plants.

Luna van Dyke Luna investigates pizza's origins, tracking its crust from flour to wheat; its cheese from milk to cow to grass; its pepperoni from pig to corn.

Way Cool Scientist Dave Forehand is a horticulturist who grows plants in air, researching techniques for growing plants by using mediums other than soil.

Music Video by FOOD WEBBY WEB performs "(It's the) Food Web."

Follow-up Questions

1. On what do all living things depend to survive? (For survival, all living things depend on plants; all living things are part of the food web.)

2. What do decomposers do? (Decomposers put important nutrients back into the soil.)

3. What is photosynthesis? (Photosynthesis is the process by which plants use carbon dioxide, sunlight, and water to make food. The byproduct of photosynthesis is oxygen.)

▲ **The Science Guy's infectious enthusiasm brings science to life.**

To order this or other Bill Nye videos, call Disney Educational Productions at 1-800-295-5010.

© Disney

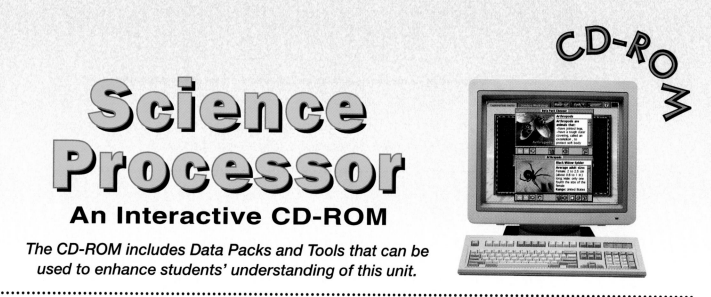

Science Processor

An Interactive CD-ROM

The CD-ROM includes Data Packs and Tools that can be used to enhance students' understanding of this unit.

Using the Data Packs

The Data Packs listed below can be accessed for information that relates to this unit. Suggest that students use the information in these packs as they write research reports that extend unit concepts.

Arthropods   **Mammals**   **Flowering Plants**
Birds   **Conifers, Cycads, Gingko**

Timer Students can time the loss of heat activity in Chapter 3.

Using the Tools

The following on-screen Tools can help students report results of activities, produce reports, or organize data.

Spreadsheet Students can organize their observations of plants and chart foods eaten in Chapter 1 activities. They can also chart the results of their beak tests and their temperature data in Chapters 2 and 3.

Grapher After entering their data in a Spreadsheet, interested students may wish to create a bar graph to show rate of heat loss for different materials in Chapter 3.

Writer Students can record their observations of pill bugs and of mold on bread in Chapter 1 activities. They can also record their predictions and hypotheses about bird beaks and pill bugs and describe their camouflaged insect in Chapter 2 activities. This tool can also be used to list changes in photographs in the neighborhood activity in Chapter 3.

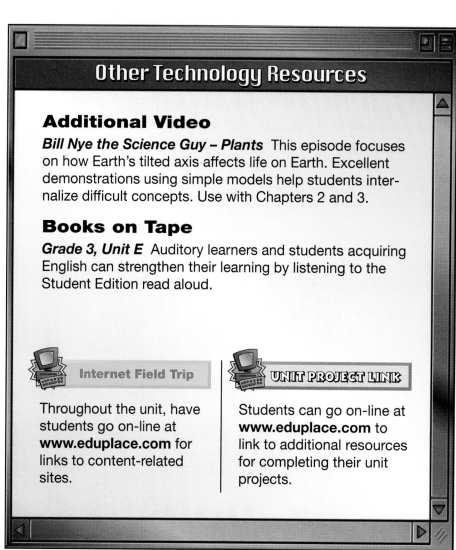

Other Technology Resources

Additional Video
Bill Nye the Science Guy – Plants This episode focuses on how Earth's tilted axis affects life on Earth. Excellent demonstrations using simple models help students internalize difficult concepts. Use with Chapters 2 and 3.

Books on Tape
Grade 3, Unit E Auditory learners and students acquiring English can strengthen their learning by listening to the Student Edition read aloud.

Internet Field Trip

Throughout the unit, have students go on-line at **www.eduplace.com** for links to content-related sites.

UNIT PROJECT LINK

Students can go on-line at **www.eduplace.com** to link to additional resources for completing their unit projects.

TEACHER-TESTED ACTIVITIES

Every Activity in Houghton Mifflin Science DiscoveryWorks *was author written, teacher reviewed, and student tested.*

Developed and Tested by Authors

The Activities in Houghton Mifflin *Science DiscoveryWorks* were developed by the program authors, and have been used by them in their own classrooms. Many of the Activities have also been used in teacher-training programs sponsored by the Center for Elementary Education at Fairleigh Dickinson University. All the Activities related to astronomy and space science have been used by students at the Houston Museum of Natural Science.

Reviewed by Teachers

All lessons and chapters in Houghton Mifflin *Science DiscoveryWorks* have been reviewed by **practicing classroom teachers**. One aspect of that review was to verify that procedures are clearly written and understandable to students and that questions are appropriate and focus on the concepts being developed. Teacher reviewers provided valuable input into the Activities, including suggestions for the type of support to provide in the Teaching Guides. A list of teacher reviewers appears at the beginning of this Teaching Guide.

Field-Tested by Students

In addition to being reviewed by teachers, all Activities in Houghton Mifflin *Science DiscoveryWorks* have been field-tested by classroom teachers in their classrooms. More than 90 teachers at 9 schools across the nation worked with the program development team during these field tests. Each activity was tested by at least two teachers in different school districts. A list of the school districts that participated in the field tests is shown below.

Science DiscoveryWorks Field-Test Sites

- Cranford Public Schools
  Cranford, NJ

- Education Center
  Dumont, NJ

- Gateway School District
  Monroeville, PA

- Dr. Charles R. Drew
  Magnet School, PS #59
  Buffalo, NY

- Mount Laurel-Hartford
  School
  Mount Laurel, NJ

- Gwinnett County Schools
  Lawrenceville, GA

- Mountain Park School
  Berkeley Heights, NJ

- Woodward School
  Saint George, UT

- Muscogee County
  School District
  Columbus, GA

MATERIALS LIST

Following is a list of materials needed for activities in this unit. Quantities are for a class of 30 students working in groups of 5. Quantities are also listed for those materials included in the Unit Kit. Additional kit options are available. Contact your sales representative for details.

Materials	Class Quantity Needed	Unit Kit Quantity	Activity Page
Consumable			
bags, plastic (self-sealing)	6	6	E15
bean plants, young	18		E6
bread	6 slices		E15
cheese	6 slices		E15
crayons or colored markers	variety		E22, E24, E46
★cups, paper	18	25	E6
★feathers, down	as needed	3 pkg	E68
★index cards	66	100	E24
magazines, discarded	as needed		E22
markers	6		E6
newspaper	as needed		E8
paper towels	1 roll		E8
paper, colored	variety		E46
pencils (colored)	variety		E22, E24, E46
pill bugs	24	25	E8
plants, young	18		E6
raisins	60		E38
★rice	1 box	1 box	E38
★sand	1 bag	1 bag	E38
★soil	1 bag	1 bag	E6
★straws, plastic	6	50	E38
string or yarn	1 ball	1 ball	E22
tape, transparent	1 roll		E8, E15, E22, E38, E46
★toothpicks	6	250	E38
★yarn, blue and red	1 skein of each	1 skein of each	E24

Materials	Class Quantity Needed	Unit Kit Quantity	Activity Page
Nonconsumable			
books, about animals	variety		E22
coat hangers, wire	30		E22
containers with lids	6		E8
flashlights	6	6	E8
★forks, plastic	6	1 pkg	E38
goggles	30	Safety Kit	E6, E8, E15, E38
hand lenses	6	6	E15
★jars, plastic (large)	12	12	E68
★jars, plastic (small)	12	12	E68
★measuring cups, 6 metric	6	6	E6, E8
★pans, rectangular	6	6	E8, E38
scissors	6		E22, E24, E38, E46
★soup spoons, plastic	6	1 pkg	E38
spoons, plastic	6	6	E8
★thermometers	12	12	E68
timers	6		E68

★ *Included in the Pressed for Time Kit.*

Roles of Living Things

Overview

In this unit, students will be learning about the relationship among living things, and how living things are adapted for getting food and for protecting themselves. They will also learn about how living things are adapted to their environments and how they can change their environment.

Reading to Learn

Unit Preview Display the KWL transparency from the *Reading Support Package*.

• Ask students what they know about living things and record their thoughts in the **K** column.

• Ask students what they want to know about living things. Record their questions in the **W** column. Be sure to include the following questions:

> **What living things are around us?**
>
> **What do living things need to live?**
>
> **What are some ways living things get food?**

• You may wish to have students complete their own KWL chart using the TRB master found on page 9. Have them fill in the **L** column of the chart when they complete the unit.

Warming Up

Explain that the photo is of an insect that blends in to its surroundings. Stimulate discussion with these questions:

> **What might happen to the leaf nymph if it were a different color, such as a bright red?**
>
> **How else do insects protect themselves from enemies?**

Tell the students that as they work through this unit, they'll find answers to these and other questions.

 Use *Science Notebook*, TRB pp. 25–26.

THINK LIKE A SCIENTIST

• Plan and Do a Test • Record and Analyze • Draw Conclusions • Make Observations • Ask a Question • Make a Hypothesis • Plan and

FIND THAT INSECT

Can you find an insect in this photo? If you look carefully, you'll see a wandering leaf nymph. It looks just like one of the plant leaves surrounding it. Animals that are able to blend in with their environment are hidden from their enemies. This leaf nymph can hide from hungry birds that could make a quick meal of it. Blending in with their environment helps animals survive to produce offspring.

E2

Home-School Connection

The Opening Letter at the beginning of the unit introduces family members to the topics of the roles of living things. Distribute the Opening Letter (TRB p. 2) at the beginning of the unit.

Dear Family,

You know what you and your family need in order to live. In this unit on the roles of living things, our science class will be discovering what plants and animals need to survive. We'll be studying (1) how plants make their own food and how animals get their food, (2) how living things protect themselves, and (3) how living things become adapted to and sometimes change their environments.

With your student, examine the plants and animals that live in your neighborhood. If you or someone you know has house plants or pets, encourage your student to observe these living things closely for features that help them survive. Examples include a cat's claws, the sharp spines and waxy covering of a cactus, and a dog's sense of smell.

For this unit, we'll be using the materials listed below. Can you donate any of these items? If so, we need to receive them by _____.

• *rectangular aluminum baking pans (disposable)*
• *newspapers and old magazines*
• *self-sealing plastic bags*
• *wire coat hangers*
• *yarn or string*
• *plastic forks, spoons, and straws*
• *toothpicks*

Do you or other family members have a special interest in or experience with roles of living things? Could you help with activities? If so, please fill out the form below and have your student return it to class.
Thank you for your help!

Opening Letter
Roles of Living Things

Your name _____ Student's name _____

Home phone _____ Work phone _____

THINK LIKE A SCIENTIST

Questioning In this unit you'll study how living things get what they need to live, and how living things change and adapt to their environment. You'll investigate questions such as these.

- How Do Living Things Get the Food They Need?
- How Are Living Things Adapted for Protection?

Observing, Testing, Hypothesizing In the Activity "Blending In," you'll find out how animals hide from their enemies. You'll also hypothesize why it is hard to find insects that blend in with their environment.

Researching In the Resource "Hiding Out and Other Defenses," you'll find out about many ways that plants and animals protect themselves from their enemies.

Drawing Conclusions After you've completed your investigations, you'll draw conclusions about what you've learned— and get new ideas.

E3

THINK LIKE A SCIENTIST

Before starting this unit, you may wish to have your students review scientific methods on pages S2–S9 found at the beginning of their book.

 Refer students to the two questions listed at the end of the *Questioning* section on page E3 of their book. Tell them that these questions are the titles of some of the Investigations in this unit.

 Have students select one of the questions and form a hypothesis that might answer that question.

Ask students **What other questions would you like to ask about living things?** You may wish to write students' questions on the chalkboard. At the end of the unit have students determine whether or not each question has been answered.

 ## BOOKS AND ARTICLES FOR TEACHERS

Ecology by Steve Polluck (Eyewitness Science, Dorling Kindersley, 1993). Beautiful photos and informative captions that describe the ways animals and plants are linked together in habitats around the world

How Nature Works by David Burnie (Reader's Digest Association, 1991). Crammed with experiments and projects students can do that explore a wide range of topics in the natural world

Macaws by Charles A. Munn (*National Geographic*, January 1994). An up-close look that describes the macaw's characteristics, adaptation to the environment, and relationship with the environment

Water Hole: Life in a Rescued Tropical Forest by Kenneth Mallory (A New England Aquarium Book, Watts, 1992). A well-told true story of saving a tropical dry forest in Guanacaste National Park in Costa Rica

---

Science in Literature

The following two books, which are featured in this unit, can be used to spark student interest in the universe.

One Small Square: African Savanna
by Donald M. Silver
Illustrated by Patricia J. Wynne and Dianne Ettl
W.H. Freeman & Co., 1994

Piranhas and Other Wonders of the Jungle
by Q.L. Pearce
Illustrated by Mary Ann Fraser
Julian Messner, 1990

CHAPTER 1

RELATIONSHIPS AMONG LIVING THINGS

Subconcepts	Activities	Materials

Investigation 1 What Do Living Things Need? pp. E6–E13

Living things need other living things and certain nonliving things to survive.
 	
Suggested Pacing: 3–4 class periods
 	
National Science Education Standards
    See page E 1c, numbers 1, 4, and 5.
 	
Project 2061 Benchmarks
    See page E 1c, numbers 1, 2, and 6.
	Needs of Plants, p. E6
	Science Process Skills: predict; infer; observe; measure/use numbers; collect, record, and interpret data; identify and control variables; define operationally; experiment
	
	A Pill Bug's Home, p. E8
	Science Process Skills: observe; infer; collect, record, and interpret data; identify and control variables; define operationally; experiment
		Needs of Plants
		marker, 3 young plants in paper cups, metric measuring cup*, *Science Notebook,* TRB pp. 29–30
		
		A Pill Bug's Home
		rectangular baking pan*, paper towels, tape, newspaper, spoon*, pill bugs in a container with lid*, flashlight*, small cup of water, *Science Notebook,* TRB pp. 31–32

Investigation 2 How Do Living Things Get the Food They Need? pp. E14–E21

Living things get their energy in various ways.
 	
Suggested Pacing: 3–4 class periods
 	
National Science Education Standards
    See page E 1c, number 1.
 	
Project 2061 Benchmarks
    See page E 1c, numbers 1, 3, and 6.
	Meat and Potatoes, p. E14
	Science Process Skills: collect, record, and interpret data; classify
	
	A Menu for Molds, p. E15
	Science Process Skills: predict; observe; collect, record, and interpret data; infer; experiment
		Meat and Potatoes
		Science Notebook, TRB p. 34
		
		A Menu for Molds
		slice of bread, slice of cheese, sealable plastic bag*, tape, hand lens*, *Science Notebook,* TRB pp. 35–36

Investigation 3 What Are Food Chains and Food Webs? pp. E22–E34

Living things are part of food chains, which are part of food webs.
 	
Suggested Pacing: 4–5 class periods
 	
National Science Education Standards
    See page E 1c, numbers 1, 2, and 6.
 	
Project 2061 Benchmarks
    See page E 1c, numbers 1, 5, and 7.
	Making a Food-Chain Mobile, p. E22
	Science Process Skills: make and use models, classify, communicate, infer, define operationally
	
	More Links in the Food Chain, p. E24
	Science Process Skills: make and use models, infer, define operationally
		Making a Food-Chain Mobile
		books about plants and animals, old magazines, scissors, crayons or colored markers, tape, yarn or string*, wire coat hanger, *Science Notebook,* TRB pp. 38–39
		
		More Links in the Food Chain
		index cards*, crayons or colored markers, short lengths of blue yarn and red yarn*, *Science Notebook,* TRB pp. 40–41

Overview

In this chapter students investigate the relationships among living things, discover how living things meet their needs, and learn that living things are part of food webs.

Chapter Concept

Living things require an environment that meets their needs; living things in an environment are interdependent.

Theme: Constancy and Change

In this chapter, students will learn that while individual plants and animals come and go, the community of plants and animals continues.

Advance Preparation	Resources/ Vocabulary	Assessment
Needs of Plants Schedule this activity to begin on a Monday. Three to five days beforehand, plant seeds in paper cups. Use bean, radish, celery, or other fast-growing seeds. Fill each cup 2/3 full of soil. Plant 2 or 3 seeds in each cup about 1 1/2 inches deep. Keep the soil in each cup moist, being careful not to overwater. Allow each cup to get sunlight. **A Pill Bug's Home** Mail the coupon* for isopods (pill bugs) at least three weeks before students will do the activity.	**A Perfect Place to Live** **Vocabulary:** habitat, environment	**Chapter 1 Baseline Assessment:** TRB pp. 27–28 **Investigation 1 Baseline Assessment,** TG p. E6 **Investigation 1 Review:** TRB p. 107 **Think It/Write It:** p. E13; TRB p. 33 **Following Up on Baseline Assessment,** TG p. E13 **Portfolio:** TG p. E13
Meat and Potatoes None **A Menu for Molds** None	**What's for Dinner?** **Vocabulary:** producers, consumer, carnivores, herbivores, omnivores, decomposers **Saber Teeth!** **Vocabulary:** extinction	**Investigation 2 Baseline Assessment:** TG p. E14 **Investigation 2 Review:** TRB p. 108 **Think It/Write It:** p. E21 TRB p. 37 **Following Up on Baseline Assessment:** TG p. E21 **Performance:** TG p. E21
Making a Food-Chain Mobile Get some books about plants and animals and some old magazines. **More Links in the Food Chain** Buy or get some short lengths of blue and red yarn.	**Who Eats Whom?** **Vocabulary:** food chain, predators, prey, food web **Cane Toads in Leaping Numbers** **Vocabulary:** community **Deadly Links**	**Investigation 3 Baseline Assessment:** TG p. E22 **Investigation 3 Review:** TRB p. 109 **Think It/Write It:** p. E34; TRB p. 43 **Following Up on Baseline Assessment:** TG p. E34 **Portfolio:** TG p. E34 **Chapter 1 Summative Assessment:** Reflect and Evaluate: E35 Chapter 1 Review/Test: TRB pp. 110–111 *Science Notebook,* TRB pp. 44–45

*Materials in the Equipment Kit TG= Teaching Guide TRB= Teacher Resource Book

Chapter Overview

Concept Preview

You may wish to use Transparency E1 to introduce some of the important concepts of the chapter. Students can add to the map as they complete each Activity and Resource. Then they can use the completed map as a study guide. See below for an example of a completed map.

Vocabulary Development

You may use Vocabulary Master E1 at any point in the chapter to provide additional support for the science vocabulary words.

Common Misconceptions

Students might think that carnivorous animals, such as wolves, do not depend on plants.

Introducing the Chapter

Warm-Up Activity

 Have small groups of students discuss an imaginary habitat with four types of living things. Wasta are thorny, red-leafed plants. Bellhoppers, small green animals, eat only Wasta. Gurgles are larger fuzzy animals that eat Wasta and Bellhoppers. Stumblysnills eat only Gurgles. Because of pollution from a nearby Zorg factory, chemicals in the soil poison the Wasta plants, but do not directly harm the animals.

• **What, if any, effect will the poison have on each type of living thing? Why?**

Use *Science Notebook,* TRB pp. 27–28.

Discussion Starter

Initiate a discussion about students' current understanding of how people affect nature.

• **If there was one environmental problem you could solve in your area, what would it be?** Students may suggest problems such as polluted rivers or lakes, litter, car exhaust, bad smells from factories, runoff from pesticides or fertilizers.

• **What actions would you take?** Students might mention writing letters or getting others to help clean up.

RELATIONSHIPS AMONG LIVING THINGS

Can there ever be too much of a good thing? Unfortunately, the answer is *yes*. Take the fertilizer that helps crops grow. As useful as it is, fertilizer can also cause harm by running off into our water supply and damaging it. Relationships, or how one thing affects another, can be tricky!

PEOPLE USING SCIENCE

National Park Ranger In 1916 the National Park Service was created to preserve national parks. This agency relies on its team of park rangers to protect the wildlife and natural scenery within the parks.

Park rangers do many different jobs. Some rangers patrol the parks to make sure that visitors don't harm or otherwise change the environment. Other park rangers, such as Erin K. Broadbent, work to inform visitors of the history and importance of preserving the parks. As a park ranger in Washington, D.C., Erin Broadbent helps preserve the environments around the national monuments, such as the Washington Monument.

As you read Chapter 1, think about how changes in the environment affect the living things around you.

E4

Concept Preview

Transparency

> **All living things need an environment that meets their needs.**
>
> **Needs of Plants** — air, nutrients, water, soil, sunlight
>
> **Needs of Animals** — air, water, food, place to live, proper temperature

▲ **Reading Support Book**
Transparency E1

Vocabulary Development

Vocabulary Master

Name _____ Date _____

Use the clues and the words in the box to complete the puzzle on page E33. When you have finished, read down the shaded column to answer the riddle.

Riddle *What did the two snakes say when they saw a rabbit?*

environment	omnivores	decomposers	community	habitat
herbivores	consumers	extinction	food chain	prey
carnivores	producers	predators	food web	

Clues
1. Overlap of food chains
2. Eat only plants
3. Where an animal or a plant lives
4. Dying out of all of a certain kind of living thing
5. Living things that eat to survive
6. Path energy takes as one living thing eats another
7. Living things that make their own food
8. Everything that surrounds and affects a living thing
9. Hunt other animals for food
10. Eat only animals
11. Eat plants and animals
12. A group of living things that depend on one another
13. Break down and feed on once-living things
14. Hunted for food by other animals

▲ **Reading Support Book**
Vocabulary Master E1

◀ Erin Broadbent realized her dream of working for the National Park Service.

E5

Chapter Road Map

INVESTIGATION 1
WHAT DO LIVING THINGS NEED?

Activities	Resources
✳ Needs of Plants A Pill Bug's Home	✳ A Perfect Place to Live

INVESTIGATION 2
HOW DO LIVING THINGS GET THE FOOD THEY NEED?

Activities	Resources
✳ Meat and Potatoes A Menu for Molds	✳ What's for Dinner? Saber Teeth!

INVESTIGATION 3
WHAT ARE FOOD CHAINS AND FOOD WEBS?

Activities	Resources
Making a Food-Chain Mobile ✳ More Links in the Food Chain	✳ Who Eats Whom? Cane Toads in Leaping Numbers Deadly Links

✳ Pressed for Time?
If you are pressed for time, focus on the Activities and Resources identified by this clock.

Home-School Connection
Distribute the Explore at Home Activity "Our Social Food Web" (Teacher Resource Book, page 3) to students after they have completed the chapter.

Correlation to AIMS
If you use AIMS Activities, you may wish to use the Activity "Catch Me If You Can" on pages 136–138 in the *Critters* book to further explore food chains.

Technology Link
Videotape

Bill Nye the Science Guy *Plants*
Bill illustrates why plants are powerhouses that keep the world alive, adding oxygen to the air, and providing food for all animals on Earth—including humans. He explains that plants are also successful at getting what they need from their environment. One experiment demonstrates that carbon dioxide is formed when we breathe, and that plants use carbon dioxide (along with water and sunlight) to make their own food. Oxygen production and seed dispersal (using animals) are also examined. (Disney Educational Productions 1-800-295-5010)

WHAT DO LIVING THINGS NEED?

pages E6–E13

Planner

Subconcept Living things need other living things and certain nonliving things to survive.

Objectives
- **Infer** what plants and animals need to survive.
- **Explain** that to survive, living things must be able to get what they need to live from their environment.

Pacing 3–4 class periods

Science Terms habitat, environment

Activate Prior Knowledge

Baseline Assessment Ask: **What kinds of plants and animals have you seen? Where have you seen them?** List the class responses and help students classify them (e.g., in woods, in deserts, in homes, on TV nature shows, in backyards, in parks). Save the list for use in Following Up.

WHAT DO LIVING THINGS NEED?

Imagine that it's a hot day and you're very thirsty. You need to drink a tall glass of water. Water is one of the things you need to live. Other living things need water, too. What else do living things need? In Investigation 1 you'll find out!

Activity

Needs of Plants

Plants seem to grow almost anywhere. What do they need to live?

MATERIALS
- goggles
- marker
- 3 young plants in paper cups
- water
- metric measuring cup
- *Science Notebook*

SAFETY
Wear goggles during this activity.

Procedure

1. With a marker, write *Soil* on a paper cup containing a young plant growing in soil. Label a second such cup *Soil + Water*. Write *Soil + Water + Sunlight* on a third cup. Make a chart like the one shown.

Conditions	Plants After One Week
Soil	
Soil + Water	
Soil + Water + Sunlight	

2. Pour 25 mL of water into the cup labeled *Soil + Water*. Pour another 25 mL of water into the cup labeled *Soil + Water + Sunlight*.

E6

Activity Needs of Plants

Preview *Students focus on plants and their growth requirements and should find that plants need soil, water, and sunlight in order to live.*

Advance Preparation *See p. E4b.*

1. Get Ready

 GROUPS OF 4–6   **30 MINUTES**

Then 5 minutes each day for one week

Key Science Process Skills predict, control variables, collect and record data, observe, conclude

---

Meeting Individual Needs

INCLUSION

Students can use their sense of touch to observe how well the plants are growing under the varying conditions. Gently grasping a leaf between the thumb and fingers will give them a good idea of whether a plant is getting enough water to grow. If the leaf feels limp, it isn't getting enough water. If it is firm, it is getting the water it needs.

KINESTHETIC

3. Place the cup labeled *Soil* and the cup labeled *Soil + Water* in a place where the plants will get no light. Place the cup labeled *Soil + Water + Sunlight* near a window. **Predict** which conditions will be best for growth. **Record** your prediction in your *Science Notebook.*

4. Every day for one week, check that the soil is moist in the cup labeled *Soil + Water* and in the cup labeled *Soil + Water + Sunlight.* Do not add water to the cup labeled *Soil.*

5. After one week, **observe** the cups to see what the plants look like. **Record** your observations.

Step 4

Analyze and Conclude

1. Under which conditions did the young plants grow best? What did those plants have that the others did not?

2. How does your prediction compare with your results? From the class results, what can you **conclude** about some of the things plants need to live and grow?

INVESTIGATE FURTHER!

EXPERIMENT

What other questions can you ask about what helps plants to grow? Form a hypothesis and then plan an experiment to test it. After your teacher approves your plan, do the experiment. Share your results with your classmates.

E7

INVESTIGATE FURTHER!

EXPERIMENT

Encourage students to think about other factors that influence plant growth, such as type of soil, the addition of fertilizer, type of water, or type of container. After each group chooses a factor to test, have them plan an experiment to test the factor. Work with students to keep their experiments simple. Students should record their observations on *Science Notebook,* TRB, p. 30.

Multi-Age Strategy Students with limited writing skills might dictate their observations to students who are more advanced to record them in the chart.

Materials Hints Make sure you use paper cups that won't fall apart from the moist soil. Use bean, radish, or other fast-growing young plants.

Safety Review safety precautions with students. Remind them to wear goggles.

2. Guide the Procedure

- Help groups find appropriate areas in the classroom where they can place the "no light" plants, such as in a closet or in a coat room. Label each set of plants with an index card showing group members' names.

- If the weather is very cloudy, have students place the "sunlight" plants under fluorescent lighting instead of near a window.

- If possible, schedule a set time every day for groups to care for their plants.

- **What do you think the information in your chart will help you learn about plants?** The chart will tell what plants need to live and grow.

- After the investigation is completed have students decide what to do with the plants. They could plant them outdoors or give them to a nursery.

 Have students record their data and answer questions on *Science Notebook,* TRB, pp. 29–30.

3. Assess Performance

Process Skills Checklist
- Did students **predict** which conditions in the activity are best for plant growth?

- Did students accurately **collect** and **record data** about plant growth? Did they note and compare the height and appearance of the plants?

- Did students **conclude** that plants need soil, water, and sunlight to grow? Were their conclusions supported by their results?

Analyze and Conclude
1. The plant that grew best was the one that had soil, water, and sunlight. The others lacked either sunlight or both water and sunlight.

2. Answers will vary. Students should conclude that plants need soil, water, and sunlight to live and grow.

Activity A Pill Bug's Home

Preview *Students focus on pill bugs and their preferred environment and find that the organisms prefer darkness and dampness to light and dryness.*

Advance Preparation *See p. E4b.*

1. Get Ready

 GROUPS OF 4–6   **20 MINUTES**

Key Science Process Skills predict; experiment; collect, record, and interpret data; observe; infer

Collaborative Strategy Students might take turns shining a flashlight on the pan and sprinkling water on the paper towels.

Materials Hints The pan should be $1\frac{1}{2}$ to 2 in. deep. Pill bugs may be purchased from a biological supply store. Alternatively, the class might go outdoors to collect pill bugs, which can be found under logs, leaves, bricks, stones, or in other dark, damp places. Collect them by moving the object under which they are hiding and scooping them up with a plastic spoon. They can be placed in a plastic container (with lid) lined with a paper towel dampened with warm water. Also note that sow bugs look like pill bugs but do not curl up when touched. You can test for this "curling" response to be sure that the specimens students collect are pill bugs.

Safety Review safety precautions with students. Tell them not to shine the light into each other's eyes. Have students wash their hands after handling the pill bugs. Remind them that pill bugs are living things which must be handled with care.

2. Guide the Procedure

- Help teams place three to six pill bugs in each pan. Also, make sure that students keep the pans level and stationary while the pill bugs are added.
- Caution students to handle the pill bugs gently.

Activity

A Pill Bug's Home

A pill bug's home keeps the pill bug safe and has the things it needs to live. Find out about two conditions that pill bugs need in this activity.

MATERIALS
- goggles
- rectangular baking pan
- paper towels
- tape
- newspaper
- spoon
- pill bugs in a container with a lid
- flashlight
- small cup of water
- *Science Notebook*

SAFETY
Wear goggles during this activity. Wash your hands when you have finished.

Procedure

1. Cover the bottom of a baking pan with paper towels. Tape the edges of the paper towels to the pan. Also seal with tape any places where the paper towels overlap. Place a sheet of newspaper over half of the top of the pan, as shown.

2. Use a spoon to carefully take 3 to 6 pill bugs, one by one, from their container and place them in the middle of the pan.

3. **Predict** whether the pill bugs will move toward light or away from light. **Record** your prediction in your *Science Notebook*. Shine a flashlight on the half of the pan not covered by newspaper. **Observe** where the pill bugs move. **Record** your observations.

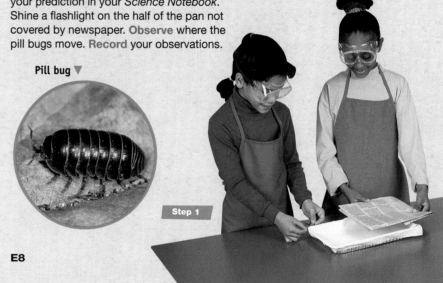

Pill bug ▼

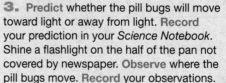

Step 1

E8

Meeting Individual Needs

GIFTED AND TALENTED

Interested students might research and report on unusual environments, such as the sea floor, mountain tops, and the Great Salt Lake. Suggest that they ask a librarian for help in finding suitable reference materials. Students can describe the environment's challenges to life and tell about plants and animals that have managed to make homes there. Allow students to choose how to best present their findings. For example, they might prepare a booklet, give an oral report, or prepare a visual presentation. Have them explain why they chose the presentation method they did.

LINGUISTIC

4. Remove the sheet of newspaper. **Predict** whether pill bugs will move toward a dry area or a wet area. **Record** your prediction. Sprinkle water on the paper towels in half of the pan to make them moist. Leave the other half of the pan dry.

5. **Observe** where the pill bugs move. **Record** your observations. Carefully use a spoon to put the pill bugs back into their container.

Step 4

Analyze and Conclude

1. How did your predictions compare with your results? Which do pill bugs prefer—light or darkness? Do they prefer moist, or dry, places?

2. From your results, what two conditions can you **infer** that pill bugs need in their homes?

3. Pill bugs live in the woods. If you went to the woods to look for them, **predict** where you would most likely find them.

Technology *Link*
CD-ROM

INVESTIGATE FURTHER!

Use the **Best of the Net— Science CD-ROM**, Life Sciences, *The Bear Den and the Cub Den* to find out how bears adapt to their environment. You'll find out where bears live. And you'll learn what some bears do when the weather gets cold.

E9

- As students do step 3, have them shine the light directly above the pan, rather than at an angle.
- Encourage students to give reasons for their predictions.
- **Why is it a good idea to observe a few pill bugs in the pan instead of just one?** Observing a few pill bugs will give a better overall idea of what pill bugs need to live. A single pill bug might behave in a way that is not usual for most pill bugs.
- After the investigation is completed have students decide what they should do with the pill bugs. They can return them to the place they were found, ask a pet store to take them, or a classroom home can be built.

Have students record their predictions and observations and answer questions on *Science Notebook*, TRB, pp. 31–32.

Science Processor Have students use the CD-ROM Spreadsheet and Painter to organize and display their data.

3. Assess Performance

Process Skills Checklist
- Did students accurately **collect** and **record data** regarding the pill bugs' responses? Did they note whether the pill bugs moved toward or away from the light and the moist towels?
- Did students **infer** that pill bugs prefer dark, moist environments? Were students' inferences about the needs of pill bugs supported by their observations?

Analyze and Conclude
1. Students may or may not have predicted that pill bugs prefer darkness over light and moistness over dryness.

2. Students should infer that pill bugs need darkness and moistness in their home.

3. Students should predict that pill bugs would be found under logs, leaves, stones, or in other dark, damp places.

Technology *Link* **CD-ROM**

INVESTIGATE FURTHER!

Students can use the **Best of the Net—Science CD-ROM**, Life Sciences, *The Bear Den* to investigate more about how bears adapt to their environment. At *The Bear Den* Web site, students discover where and how bears live, how many bears live in the wild, what they are really like, the foods they eat, and what happens when bears hibernate. Students can also visit *The Club Den* page that contains facts and information geared to young readers. Students can complete an activity in which they record information about different types of bears and what adaptations have helped them survive.

A Perfect Place to Live

Reading Focus As they read, have students look for statements in the text that *compare and contrast* the needs of living things.

1. Get Ready

Vocabulary

Science Terms habitat, environment

Support Terms tropical rain forest, desert, bacteria

Background

• Many animals that live in very dry environments have adapted different ways to get enough water to live. In the Namib Desert of southwest Africa live black beetles that get their drinking water most ingeniously. They sit on top of sand dunes where coastal fogs are common. When the moist air rolls in, they arrange themselves with their heads down and their backs facing the fog. As the damp fog strikes the beetles' tilted backs, drops of water condense on their backs and run down into their mouths.

Discussion Starter

• **Think about plants whose parts are wet: watermelon, lettuce, celery, and cucumber, for example. Could these plants live in a desert without being watered by humans? Explain.** Students should say no. These plants need more water than a desert environment provides naturally.

• **Think about fish, octopuses, and other animals that live in water. Could these animals live on land? Explain.** These animals could not live on land because their bodies would dry out or they would not be able to get the food they need. Some students may also mention that these animals would suffocate because they can get oxygen only through water.

A Perfect Place to Live

Reading Focus How are the needs of living things alike, and how do their needs differ?

What do you really need? Perhaps you need a haircut. But you have more basic needs than that. Food, water, and air are some of the things you *really* need. Other living things need food, water, and air, too.

Living things also need a place to live. The place where an animal or a plant lives is its **habitat** (hab'i tat). Everything that surrounds and affects a living thing is its **environment** (en vī'rən mənt). All living things need an environment that is suited to their needs.

Salty or Not, Cold or Hot

Living things often have very different needs. So an environment that is good for one living thing may not be good for another. For example, all water animals need a water environment. But most dolphins need to live in salt water. The ocean is a good environment for most dolphins. Other water animals, such as lake trout, small-mouth bass, and minnows, would die in salt water. They need to live in the fresh water of lakes and streams.

This dolphin lives in the ocean. ▼

E10

Science Around the World

KEEPING COOL

What to Do Have students list or draw ways in which people in different parts of the world protect themselves from sunlight and heat.

What's the Result? Students can share lists or drawings, which may include wearing sunblock, sunglasses, hats, and loose-fitting, light-weight, long-sleeved clothing. **Why might it be difficult for people to live in the desert?** It's hot and dry. Tell students that some people who live in the Sahara or Arabian Deserts wear white from head to toe. **Why might wearing white clothing from head to toe keep people cooler than wearing little clothing?** Since the skin needs protection, and white reflects light rather than absorbs it, wearing white feels cooler than not covering the skin.

▲ Life in a freshwater lake

A spotted moray eel ▼

E11

Some water animals need to live near the surface of the water, where light from the Sun keeps the water warm. Others need to live near the bottom. If you've ever gone fishing, you may know that bass need the warm water near the surface. But lake trout need the colder waters that are found at the bottom of a lake.

Many animals share the same habitat. The spotted moray eel lives in the warm, shallow ocean waters around coral reefs. Reef sharks, butterflyfish, batfish, and hogfish live in this habitat, too.

Science & Social Studies

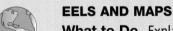

EELS AND MAPS

What to Do Explain that most fish live either in salt water or fresh water, but a few move from one habitat to another. The common eels of Europe and North America live in rivers and streams that empty into the Atlantic Ocean, but return to the Sargasso Sea (northeast of the West Indies) to breed. They lay their eggs and die, leaving the leaf-shaped eel larvae to make their way back toward the coasts to the rivers and streams. Help students locate the Atlantic coasts of North America and Europe on a world map. Then have students locate the Sargasso Sea.

What's the Result? Ask a volunteer to trace the migration routes of the adult eels, as well as the return routes of the eel larvae.

2. Guide the Discussion

Choose from the following strategies to facilitate discussion.

Connecting to the Activities

- *A Pill Bug's Home, pp. E8–E9*
- **How did the pill bugs respond to the moist towel in the pan? Could pill bugs live in a desert? Explain.** Pill bugs need a moist environment, so they could not live in a desert, which is very dry.

Making Inferences

- **Why do you think the water in a lake is warmer near the surface than at the bottom?** The surface water is warmed by sunlight.

Drawing Conclusions

- **The country of Kuwait has no rivers or lakes. Even though Kuwait is located next to an ocean, the people in this country have had to search for ways to meet their need for drinking water. Why do you think they are unable to drink the ocean water?** Ocean water is unsuitable for humans to drink because it contains too much salt.

- **How is your environment suited to your needs?** Students' responses should include how they get food, water, air, and other basic needs from their environment.

 Meeting Individual Needs

Students Acquiring English Have students draw a picture of an animal in its environment, showing how or where it gets water, food, and air. Write the words water, food, and air on the chalkboard and review their pronunciation and spelling. Students can refer to the words to help them label their drawings.

 Science Processor Suggest students use the CD-ROM Painter to make their drawings.

Making Inferences

- **Think about what plants need to grow. Should people plant a vegetable garden in the shady woods or in the middle of a cleared space? Why?** Students may respond that vegetables, such as beans, should be planted in clear spaces because these plants need a lot of sunshine to grow.

- **What do you think happens to the plants and animals in a particular place when the environment changes; for example, when a rain forest is cut down? Why?** Students may respond that the plants die and the animals may either die or move away because the environment no longer provides them with what they need.

Making Comparisons

- **What are some ways plants and animals are different?** Most plants make their own food; animals eat plants or other animals. Plants stay in one place; animals can move about. They have different body parts.

- **What are some ways plants and animals are alike?** Both plants and animals need food or nutrients, water, and air to live and grow.

Drawing Conclusions

- **Picture a farm with fields, pastures, and creeks. Now the farm and creeks are gone, and the land is covered with homes, roads, and lawns. Describe how the changed environment might affect the birds, other wildlife, and plants.** Students may reply that the environment will no longer be suitable for many living things. For example, birds will find fewer insects and seeds for food, the birds and other animals will miss the creeks for drinking water, and there will be less space for wild plants to grow.

3. Assess Understanding

Encourage students to illustrate various environments and include some of the inhabitants described in the student text. Artists can present their work to the class, describe the environment's limitations, and tell how the plants and animals survive there.

Reading Focus Answer

All living things need food, water, and air, but they differ in the kind of environment that best suits those needs.

Turn Off the Lights, Please!

Some living things need a lot of sunlight, and some need darkness. The activity on pages E6 and E7 proves that plants need sunlight to live. Without sunlight, plants couldn't make food and would die.

Different kinds of living things need different amounts of sunlight. For example, some kinds of flowers need shade. Other kinds need a lot of bright sunlight.

Pill bugs, which are observed in the activity on pages E8 and E9, need to live in a place that is dark and moist. Pill bugs will dry out in bright sunlight.

▲ A tropical rain forest in Costa Rica

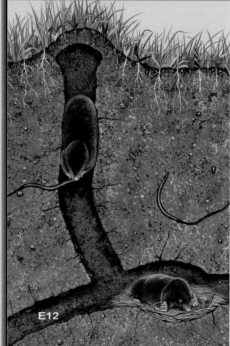
Moles live underground. ▼

E12

Some types of animals dig down into the soil to live in underground habitats. Animals such as earthworms need a dark, moist habitat. These animals would dry up and die in the bright, hot sunlight.

Moles also live underground. A mole is almost blind but has a keen sense of smell. A mole digs until it can smell the tiny insects and worms that are its food.

Very Wet or Very Dry

Some plants need a lot of rain, and others need almost no rain. The plants of the tropical rain forest need to be warm and wet. And they are! It rains almost every day of the year in the rain forest.

Science & Math

GRAPHING

What to Do Gather the plants that were grown with water and sunlight and those that were grown with water only. Tell students to use a ruler to measure the height of one plant from the tip of its stem to where the stem meets the soil. Record the heights of the two kinds of plants in separate columns on the chalkboard. Then help students calculate the average height of the plants grown under each condition.

What's the Result? Help students make a bar graph that compares the average heights of the two kinds of plants. **Why do you think the plants that had sunlight were taller than those that had no sunlight?** Plants need sunlight to make their food. The food helps them grow.

▲ Desert plants need very little rain.

Other plants need a dry place to live. The teddy bear cholla, shown above, is a cactus that grows in the desert. It rains very little in the desert. But that's fine for a cactus. They don't need a lot of water.

Too Tiny to See

All living things need a suitable environment—even living things too small to see with just the eyes. Bacteria (bak tir′ē ə) are living things that can't be seen without a microscope. Bacteria are everywhere. They can be found living in soil, air, water, and even in your body. To survive, bacteria need a warm and wet environment.

From bacteria to whales, living things need an environment that meets their needs. You know that living things need food, water, and air. They also need a way to get rid of wastes. What needs do you have? ■

Bacteria need warmth and moisture. ▼

INVESTIGATION 1 WRAP-UP

REVIEW **1.** Name three basic needs of living things.

2. How does a plant's or animal's environment help it to survive?

CRITICAL THINKING **3.** Think about two different animals that have the same needs and live in the same habitat. What things in their environment would they compete for?

4. You plant grass in soil that is shaded by trees. The grass sprouts but turns yellow. What might be causing the problem?

E13

Assessment

Portfolio

Make a Diagram Invite students to make a diagram that compares the amount of vegetation in a desert (a dry place) and in a tropical rain forest (a wet place). The diagrams should show how the plants differ in appearance and number in the two kinds of environments.

Investigation Review ▶
Use Investigation Review p. 107 in the *Teacher Resource Book*.

Investigation Review

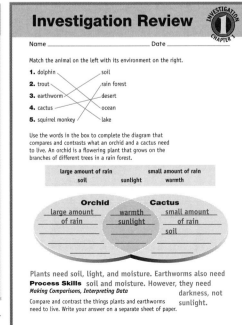

Name _____ Date _____

Match the animal on the left with its environment on the right.

1. dolphin   soil
2. trout   rain forest
3. earthworm   desert
4. cactus   ocean
5. squirrel monkey lake

Use the words in the box to complete the diagram that compares and contrasts what an orchid and a cactus need to live. An orchid is a flowering plant that grows on the branches of different trees in a rain forest.

| large amount of rain | | small amount of rain |
| soil | sunlight | warmth |

Orchid **Cactus**
large amount of rain | warmth sunlight | small amount of rain soil

Plants need soil, light, and moisture. Earthworms also need soil and moisture. However, they need darkness, not sunlight.

Process Skills
Making Comparisons, Interpreting Data

Compare and contrast the things plants and earthworms need to live. Write your answer on a separate sheet of paper.

Close the Investigation

INVESTIGATION WRAP-UP

REVIEW
1. All living things need food, water, and air.

2. Animals or plants survive best in an environment that suits all of their needs.

CRITICAL THINKING
3. Students should list things such as food, water, or living space. For example, squirrels and birds compete for seeds to eat, trees to live in, and water to drink. *(Analyzing, Synthesizing, Applying)*

4. Students should realize that plants require water and sunlight to live. The grass probably did not receive enough water or sunlight. *(Applying, Generating Ideas, Solving Problems)*

CHALLENGE

Have students find small soil-dwelling animals by shaking a handful of garden soil through a kitchen strainer onto both white and dark paper. Have students observe the soil animals through a hand lens and then repeat the pill bug activity using the animals they find in the soil. After the activity, have students return the soil and animals to where they came from and wash their hands. How many different animals did they see? Did each prefer light and dry conditions?

FOLLOWING UP

Baseline Assessment Return to the list of plants and animals students have seen. Ask students to describe the type of habitat or environmental conditions each organism needs to survive. Then have them list three different plants or animals that live in an area different from their own and describe the organisms' natural habitat. Assist by providing books about plants and animals that live in various habitats.

Reteaching Have students draw a picture of a habitat in which a plant or an animal lives. Then have them list everything that surrounds and affects their plant or animal. Remind students that a habitat is a home and an environment is all the things that surround and affect the living thing in their home.

Use *Science Notebook*, TRB p. 33.

Start
the Investigation

HOW DO LIVING THINGS GET THE FOOD THEY NEED?

pages E14–E21

Planner

Subconcept Living things get their energy in various ways.

Objectives
- **Classify** foods as of plant or animal origin.
- **Describe** how decomposers change food.
- **Compare and contrast** herbivores, carnivores, omnivores, and decomposers.

Pacing 3–4 class periods

Science Terms producers, consumers, carnivores, herbivores, omnivores, decomposers, extinction

Activate Prior Knowledge

Baseline Assessment Ask students to make a list of foods they like. Save lists for use in Following Up.

HOW DO LIVING THINGS GET THE FOOD THEY NEED?

When you are very hungry, what are your favorite foods? Living things get food in different ways. Where does your food come from? What are some ways other living things get food? Find out in Investigation 2!

MATERIALS
- *Science Notebook*

Activity

Meat and Potatoes

Do you eat plants, animals, or both? Find out by doing this activity.

What I Eat	
Food	**From Plant or Animal**

Procedure

In your *Science Notebook*, **make a chart** like the one shown. **Predict** whether most foods you eat come from plants or animals. For one week, **record** the kinds of foods you eat. List each part of a food and tell where it comes from. At the end of the week, share your observations with your classmates.

Analyze and Conclude

Do most of the foods you eat come from plants or from animals? How does your prediction compare with your findings?

E14

Activity
Meat and Potatoes

Preview *Students find that more than half of their food probably comes from plants.*

1. Get Ready

 INDIVIDUAL   15 MINUTES

Key Science Process Skills predict, record, describe, classify

Collaborative Strategy Suggest students trade charts to verify whether each food item was correctly classified as coming from either a plant or an animal.

2. Guide the Procedure

Have students record their data and answer questions on *Science Notebook*, TRB, p. 34.

3. Assess Performance

Process Skills Checklist
- Did students **record** everything they ate over a one-week period?
- Did students accurately **classify** the foods they ate as coming from a plant or an animal?

Analyze and Conclude
Most foods probably come from plants. Students may have predicted more animal foods than results showed.

Activity

A Menu for Molds

Do this activity to find out how living things called molds get food.

MATERIALS
- goggles
- bread (1 slice)
- cheese (1 slice)
- sealable plastic bag
- tape
- hand lens
- *Science Notebook*

SAFETY

Wear goggles during this activity. Some molds are harmful. Do not open the bag containing the food.

Procedure

1. Place one slice of moist bread and one slice of cheese in a sandwich bag. Seal the bag and tape it closed. Put the bag in a warm, dark place for one week. **Predict** what will happen to the foods in the bag. **Record** your prediction in your *Science Notebook*.

2. After one week, use a hand lens to **observe** the foods in the bag. Look for mold. *Do not open the bag.*

 See **SCIENCE** and **MATH TOOLBOX** page H2 if you need to review **Using a Hand Lens.**

3. **Make drawings** of what you see. **Describe** how the food has changed.

4. Put the bag back in the same warm, dark place for another week. Repeat steps 2 and 3 at the end of the second week.

Step 1

Step 2

Analyze and Conclude

1. What happened to the food in the bag? **Compare** your prediction with your results.

2. From your results, **infer** what the molds you saw used for food.

3. **Predict** what would happen to the food if you left it in the bag for several months.

E15

Meeting Individual Needs

STUDENTS ACQUIRING ENGLISH

Allow students to draw their predictions of what the bread and cheese will look like after one and two weeks. Then help students write a sentence describing their pictures. They can use their predictions at the end of the activity to compare with the drawings they made of their observations. Display their two drawings side by side. Help students compare their results with their predictions.

VISUAL/SPATIAL

 Science Processor Encourage students to use the CD-ROM Painter to make their drawings.

Activity A Menu for Molds

Preview *Students focus on how bread and cheese are consumed by mold as they decay.*

1. Get Ready

 GROUPS OF 4–6   **15 MINUTES**

Then 15 minutes after 1 week and then again after 2 weeks

Key Science Process Skills predict, identify and control variables, record, describe, compare, infer

Multi-Age Strategy Have students who are more adept at recognizing variables put one bag in a warm, dark place and the other in a refrigerator. Then compare and explain any observed differences.

Safety Remind students to wear goggles, examine the food through the closed plastic bags, and wash their hands when they have finished. Proper handling and disposal of decayed food is imperative.

2. Guide the Procedure

- Label bags with students' names. Place the bags where they won't be disturbed.
- When students have completed the activity, dispose of the sealed sandwich bags in a sealed trash bag in a trash container.

 Have students record their predictions and observations and answer questions on *Science Notebook*, TRB, pp. 35–36.

3. Assess Performance

Process Skills Checklist
- Did students make reasonable **predictions** as to what would happen to the food in the bag?
- Did students **infer** what the molds used for food, based on their observations?

Analyze and Conclude
1. The food was eaten by molds.
2. Molds use once-living things for food.
3. Students should predict that more of the bread and cheese would be eaten by the molds.

What's for Dinner?

1. Get Ready

Vocabulary

Science Terms producers, consumer, carnivores, herbivores, omnivores, decomposers

Support Terms roots, leaves, iguanas

Background

- One group of plants forms an exception to the rule that plants are producers—the insect-eating plants. Pitcher plants, cobra plants, sundews, and Venus' flytraps all live in nitrogen-poor soils. They capture and digest flying insects to obtain the nitrogen they need. For example, a Venus' flytrap captures insects with its traplike leaves. Each leaf has sensitive hairs that detect when an insect has alighted on the leaf. In response, the leaf closes shut and traps the insect inside. The insect is then digested by fluids released by the leaf.

Discussion Starter

- **What do pets eat?** Students might reply that pet snakes eat mice; dogs and cats eat pet food made from cereal or from animal parts; birds eat seeds; fish eat fish food flakes; and so on.

- **What do you think your pet would eat if it had grown up in the wild?** Students might say that dogs and cats would probably eat birds, mice, and fish; fish might eat smaller fish or water plants; and snakes would probably continue eating mice but would have to hunt for them.

What's for Dinner?

Plants make their own food. ▼

Imagine never needing to eat breakfast, lunch, or dinner! If you were a plant, you would never need to eat. You would make your own food.

Food Makers

Plants make their own food inside their leaves. Plants take in water and air from their environment. The leaves soak up sunlight. Plants use the Sun's energy to make food from water and a gas in the air. This food can be stored in roots, leaves, and other plant parts for use later on.

Living things that can make their own food are called **producers** (prō dōōs'ərz). Plants are producers. Producers make up the basic food supply in the environment. Without them, most other kinds of living things would not be able to exist.

May I See a Menu?

Since your body can't produce its own food, as a plant does, you have to get it another way—by eating something else. That means that you are a consumer (kən sōōm'ər).

E16

Science & Writing

PRESENTATIONS

What to Do Interested students could research the process plants use to produce their own food. Suggest that they ask a librarian for help in finding suitable reference materials. Students should find out what the plants need and how they use these things to make their food. Ask the students to choose a way to teach what they found out to the rest of the class. For example, they might write a report, make a booklet, or prepare a visual presentation.

What's the Result? Encourage students to evaluate the presentations including the appropriateness of the medium. **How else could the information be presented?**

A **consumer** is a living thing that eats plants, animals, or other living things.

What kinds of things are usually on your dinner plate? Crunchy crickets and other insects? You might eat these animals if you were a praying mantis. A praying mantis is an animal eater. Animals that eat only other animals are called **carnivores** (kär′nə vôrz). Spiders, many insects, and some worms are carnivores. Cats, snakes, wolves, owls, and many fish are carnivores, too.

◄ A praying mantis is a carnivore.

Wolves are carnivores. ▼

E17

Science & Writing

LISTING GAME

What to Do Let students work in small groups to list plants and animals they know. They can play a circle game in which each person names a plant or animal that begins with the last letter of the previous person's plant or animal; for example, butterfly, yam, mountain lion, and so on.

What's the Result? Have students write a list of common plants and animals. Then write whether each animal is a herbivore, carnivore, or omnivore.

Multi-Age Classroom Group students by age. Older students may play the game as described above. Younger students may take turns naming plants or animals in alphabetical order.

2. Guide the Discussion

Choose from the following strategies to facilitate discussion.

Connecting to the Activities
- *A Menu for Molds, p. E15*
- **Was the mold that you observed in the activity a producer or a consumer? How do you know?** The mold was a consumer because it did not make its own food. It fed on the bread and cheese.

Making Comparisons
- **What do you think is an advantage of being a producer? a consumer?** Students might say that a producer does not have to look for or chase after food. A consumer can eat a variety of foods and travel to find these foods.

Meeting Individual Needs

For Extra Help Show students photographs of the teeth of herbivores and carnivores as well as some kinds of food the animals eat, such as leaves and seeds (herbivores) and small and large animals (carnivores). Direct students to suggest which tooth is best suited for eating each type of food. Help students recognize that herbivores have flat grinding teeth that help them grind seeds and tough plant fibers. Carnivores have sharp piercing teeth that help them kill prey quickly and tear off chunks of meat.

Making Inferences

- **From the names of the following plants and animals, try to decide what each plant or animal eats or is eaten by: cotton aphid, bearberry, European corn borer, European cabbage butterfly, Great Crested flycatcher, American oyster catcher.** Students should infer as follows (in order): eats cotton, food of bears, eats corn plants, eats cabbage plants, eats flies, eats oysters.

- **Why might a person choose to be a herbivore?** Students might respond that the person might not like the taste of meat, might be against killing an animal for food, or might not think that eating meat is healthy.

- **What advantage might an animal have being an omnivore rather than a herbivore or carnivore?** The animal would have a greater variety of food to choose from.

 ### Meeting Individual Needs

Students Acquiring English Invite students to look through old magazines and find pictures to make posters that show pictures of herbivores, carnivores, and omnivores. Have students write a definition of their animal group. Display the posters around the room to reinforce the concepts with all students.

Brown bears sometimes eat plants. ▼

Prairie dogs do not eat other animals. They crawl out of their underground burrows and feed on plants. Marine iguanas (i gwä′nəz) also eat only plants, enjoying a meal of salty seaweed. Animals such as prairie dogs and marine iguanas are called herbivores (hʉr′bə vôrz). A **herbivore** is an animal that eats only plants. Elephants and horses are herbivores. So are caterpillars and deer. What other plant-eating animals can you think of?

Many animals are omnivores (äm′ni vôrz). **Omnivores** are animals that eat both plants and animals. Brown bears are omnivores. They eat berries and other fruits, but they also eat small animals, like fish.

Raccoons are also omnivores. So are some types of mice, birds, and turtles. The activity on page E14 investigates whether the food people eat comes from plants, animals, or both. If you eat both plants and animals, you're an omnivore, too!

Breaking It Down

In every environment there is an important group of consumers called decomposers (dē kəm pōz′ərz). **Decomposers** feed on the remains of once-living things. Bacteria, mushrooms, yeast, and molds are decomposers. Molds grow on foods that haven't been stored in the right way. Mold is grown in the activity on page E15. What can you do to prevent molds from growing?

Brown bears eat fish, too. ▼

E18

Integrating the Sciences

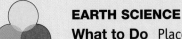

EARTH SCIENCE

What to Do Place some garden soil on a sheet of white paper. Invite students to use a hand lens to observe the particles in the soil. Direct them to look for evidence of decayed plant or animal matter, such as bits of leaves, twigs, and insect parts. Have students list what they find. Tell students to wash their hands after handling the soil.

What's the Result? Encourage students to draw pictures of the soil particles under the hand lens. Ask them to include any plant or animal matter they observed. Discuss students' findings, including items that some students found and others did not.

▲ A raccoon is an omnivore.

Decomposers are important to the environment. They break down materials from once-living things into simpler materials. Decomposers release these simpler materials back into the water, soil, and air, where they can be used again by other living things. Rotting logs and rotting leaves on the forest floor are signs that decomposers have been at work. ■

Mushrooms are decomposers. ▶

E19

Identifying and Solving Problems

- **What do decomposers need to live?** Based on their knowledge of plants and animals, students should conclude that decomposers need food, water, and air to live. Point out to students that most decomposers, however, are neither plants nor animals.

Making Inferences

- **Plants use the simple materials that decomposers return into the soil. They use these materials to live and grow. How do you think they take in these materials?** Plants take in materials from the soil through their roots.

Drawing Conclusions

- **If there were no decomposers on Earth, what do you think would happen to living things when they died? What effect would this have on Earth?** The living things would not be broken down into simpler materials needed by other living things. Earth would become full of dead plants and animals and other once-living things.

3. Assess Understanding

Students can work in groups of four or five. Ask each group to list living things that at least one kind of consumer uses for food; for example, hay (elephant) or leaves (earthworm). Have the groups include one or more nonfood items in their lists (items that have no known consumers, such as rocks or metal objects) and present their food lists without showing any corresponding consumers. Groups can challenge each other to find the nonfood items on their lists.

Reading Focus Answer

You can classify living things, according to what they eat, as herbivores, carnivores, omnivores, or decomposers.

Science Around the World

DIFFERENT FOODS

What to Do Explain that in the past and today, many people around the world eat foods that other groups would consider distasteful. Let students suggest some examples. Then mention that long ago in Europe and Central and South America, and today in China, Africa, and Australia, some people eat different kinds of insects. Explain that insects are an excellent source of protein and some vitamins. However, people elsewhere would not consider eating insects. Another example is cheese, which many Asians will not eat as they consider it rotten milk.

What's the Result? Ask students to suggest other foods they would consider distasteful. If they have not tried these foods, discuss why they would be reluctant to do so.

Saber Teeth!

Reading Focus As students read the text on page E21, have them look for words, such as *compare*, *both*, and *differently*, that signal statements that *compare and contrast*.

1. Get Ready

Vocabulary
Science Term extinction
Support Terms prey, bog

Background
• A saber-toothed cat or *Smilodon* is the state fossil of California. Explain to students that many kinds of living things that once lived on Earth have completely disappeared, but some of these living things resembled others that are alive today.

2. Guide the Discussion

Connecting to the Activities
• *Meat and Potatoes, p. E14*
• **How was the diet of the saber-toothed cat different from the diet of most humans today?** Humans are omnivores, eating meat and vegetables. Saber-toothed cats were carnivores that hunted prey.

Caption answer: The saber-toothed cat skull is flatter with longer teeth, but both are the same length.

3. Assess Understanding

In groups of two, have students create diagrams that compare and contrast the modern African lion and the saber-toothed cat.

Reading Focus Answer

The saber-toothed cat and the African lion are about the same size and both were predators.

Internet Field Trip
From **www.eduplace.com** students can link to a Web site about saber-toothed cats and how they lived. A trip log will guide their visit to the site.

Saber Teeth!

Reading Focus How were saber-toothed cats similar to African lions?

The cat watches its prey, waiting for the right moment to attack. Finally, it uses its short but powerful legs to leap onto the grazing animal. The heavy weight of the cat brings down its prey, a bison, in an instant. The cat uses its knifelike 23-cm (9-inch) teeth to slash into the belly of the bison.

This is no ordinary cat. It's a saber-toothed cat. But you won't see any of these cats around today. They became extinct around 11,000 years ago.

This bison, trapped in a tar pit, is about to be attacked by a saber-toothed cat. ▼

Extinction (ek stiŋk′shen) is the dying out of all living things of a certain kind. Can you think of any other animals that are extinct?

Scientists learn about saber-toothed cats by studying their remains, which are mostly preserved bones. Such remains are called fossils. Scientists have found many fossils in a place in California called the La Brea Tar Pits.

The La Brea Tar Pits is a bog, a place where the ground is wet and spongy. Water covers the bog. The tar pits contain a tarlike substance. Scientists have found thousands of bones from extinct animals, including saber-toothed cats, in the tar pits. Why are there so many fossils at La Brea?

E20

Science & Writing

CREATIVE WRITING

What to Do Have students do library research to find out more about extinct animals: the environment in which they lived, what they ate, and how they became extinct. Have students choose an extinct animal and then list an animal of today that resembles it. Students can choose dinosaurs or other prehistoric animals or they may choose animals that have become extinct in the last 200 years, such as the dodo, the passenger pigeon, and the Carolina parakeet.

What's the Result? Have students use their findings to write a short story or poem. They should present their story or poem in a dramatic reading to the class.

▲ Compare the skull of the extinct saber-toothed cat to that of the modern African lion. What are the differences? What are the similarities?

Although saber-toothed cats are extinct, there are big cats alive today. These cats are something like those extinct cats. Compare the modern African lion, top right, to the saber-toothed cat, top left. They are both about the same size but the saber-toothed cat had shorter, more powerful legs. It also had a shorter tail and weighed almost twice as much as an African lion.

Scientists think that the saber-toothed cat hunted differently than a lion. It's likely that the saber-toothed cat was not as fast as today's big cats. It probably did not chase its prey. A saber-toothed cat most likely waited and watched for its prey to come close. When that prey came close enough, the big cat would pounce on it. ■

Internet Field Trip
Visit **www.eduplace.com** to learn more about how saber-toothed cats lived.

─── INVESTIGATION 2 WRAP-UP ───

REVIEW

1. What is a producer? What is a consumer? Which one are you? Explain your answer.

2. Compare the diets of carnivores, herbivores, and omnivores.

CRITICAL THINKING

3. Could carnivores live if all plants became extinct? Why or why not?

4. If scientists found the skeleton of an unknown animal, what clues would help them find out what kinds of foods the animal ate?

E21

═══ Assessment ═══

Performance

Design Let students work in small groups to design a zoo with herbivores, carnivores, and omnivores. They might make a blueprint or a diorama with clay models. Encourage students to discuss what the animals might be fed, and the type of environment that would be suitable for housing each animal. Invite groups to share their designs with the class.

Investigation Review ▶
Use Investigation Review p. 108 in the *Teacher Resource Book*.

Investigation Review

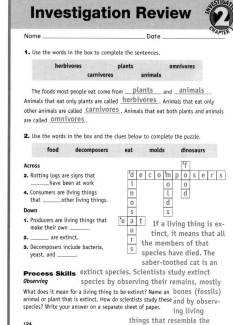

Name _____ Date _____

1. Use the words in the box to complete the sentences.

herbivores	plants	omnivores
	carnivores	animals

The foods most people eat come from <u>plants</u> and <u>animals</u>. Animals that eat only plants are called <u>herbivores</u>. Animals that eat only other animals are called <u>carnivores</u>. Animals that eat both plants and animals are called <u>omnivores</u>.

2. Use the words in the box and the clues below to complete the puzzle.

food	decomposers	eat	molds	dinosaurs

Across
2. Rotting logs are signs that _____ have been at work
4. Consumers are living things that _____ other living things.

Down
1. Producers are living things that make their own _____.
2. _____ are extinct.
3. Decomposers include bacteria, yeast, and _____.

If a living thing is extinct, it means that all the members of that species have died. The saber-toothed cat is an extinct species. Scientists study extinct species by observing their remains, mostly bones (fossils) and by observing living things that resemble the extinct species.

Process Skills
Observing
What does it mean for a living thing to be extinct? Name an animal or plant that is extinct. How do scientists study these species? Write your answer on a separate sheet of paper.

124

INVESTIGATION WRAP-UP

REVIEW

1. Students should indicate that a producer, such as a plant, is a living thing that can make its own food. A consumer, like themselves, is a living thing that eats plants, animals, or both.

2. Students should understand that animals that eat only other animals are carnivores; animals that eat only plants are herbivores; and animals that eat both plants and animals are omnivores.

CRITICAL THINKING

3. Students should indicate that the extinction of plants would eliminate the food source for herbivores. Then the carnivores that preyed on the herbivores would, therefore, have no food source and would die. *(Analyzing, Synthesizing, Expressing Ideas)*

4. Students should indicate that teeth offer valuable clues to the types of food eaten by an animal. They may also include other body parts such as claws, bills, jaws, and legs specially adapted to obtaining food or prey. *(Evaluating, Solving Problems)*

CHALLENGE

Provide students with magazine pictures of animals. Ask them to predict whether each animal is a carnivore, herbivore, or omnivore and what the animal might eat. Direct students to library references such as encyclopedias and age-appropriate books about animals to find out whether their predictions are correct.

FOLLOWING UP

Baseline Assessment Return to the class list of foods students like. For each food, ask students to identify if it comes from a producer, omnivore, herbivore, or carnivore. Discuss foods that contain ingredients that may come from several sources.

Reteaching Have students work individually or in pairs to make a concept map that shows the relationship between producers and consumers and highlights the differences among herbivores, carnivores, omnivores, and decomposers. Students should use the "Web" on TRB p. 12.

Use *Science Notebook,* TRB p. 37.

Start
the Investigation

WHAT ARE FOOD CHAINS AND FOOD WEBS?
pages E22–E34

Planner

Subconcept Living things are part of food chains, which are part of food webs.

Objectives
- **Identify** the sequence of feeding relationships in a food chain.
- **Describe** how food chains form food webs.
- **Explain** how a change in one part of a food chain might affect the rest of the food chain.

Pacing 4–5 class periods

Science Terms food chain, predators, prey, food web, community

Activate Prior Knowledge

Baseline Assessment Ask: **What herbivores can you name? What carnivores do you know that eat those herbivores?** List the class responses and save them for use in Following Up.

WHAT ARE FOOD CHAINS AND FOOD WEBS?

Slurp! The fast tongue of a frog catches a juicy fly. Gulp! A snake eats the frog. Will the snake become a meal for some other animal? In Investigation 3 you'll explore different eating relationships.

Activity

Making a Food-Chain Mobile

Do you eat hamburgers, fruit, and salad? No matter what you eat, you're part of a food chain. Do this activity to find out more about food chains.

MATERIALS
- books about plants and animals
- old magazines
- scissors
- crayons or colored markers
- tape
- yarn or string
- wire coat hanger
- *Science Notebook*

Procedure

1. In your *Science Notebook*, make a list of four living things. First, list one kind of plant. Then, think about the kind of animal that would eat that plant. List that animal. Next, think about an animal that would eat the animal you listed. List the second animal. Now do the same for a third animal. Get ideas by looking through animal books and magazines or from your own observations.

E22

Activity Making a Food-Chain Mobile

Preview *Students focus on following energy through living things in a food chain and find that food chains begin with producers.*

Advance Preparation *see p. E4b.*

1. Get Ready

 GROUPS OF 4–6   **30 MINUTES**

Key Science Process Skills model, classify, infer

 ## Meeting Individual Needs

EARLY FINISHERS

Help students understand the concepts in this investigation by encouraging them to make up a rhythmic version of a food chain. Try something like this: "The wren swallowed the wheat, the jay swallowed the wren, the hawk swallowed the jay, and the owl swallowed the hawk" or "The bug was eaten by the chicken, the chicken was eaten by the fox, the fox was eaten by the wolf, the wolf was eaten by the bear, and the bear was eaten by me."

Multi-Age Classroom Some students may be able to recite descriptions of food chains that also rhyme. If possible, allow students to use various percussion instruments, such as triangles and drums, to play along with their rhymes and rhythms.

AUDITORY

2. Cut out pictures from old magazines or **draw** pictures of the four living things in your food chain. Then tape your pictures to a piece of yarn, as shown. Put the living things in order of who eats whom. Think back to Investigation 2 to help you decide what should be at the bottom of your food chain. Tape the end of the yarn to a wire hanger. You've made a food-chain mobile.

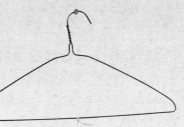

Analyze and Conclude

1. Which living thing is the producer in your food chain?

2. Which living things are consumers?

3. Look at the food-chain mobiles of your classmates. What can you **infer** about the kind of living thing that is at the bottom of a food chain?

Step 2

E23

Science, Technology & Society

STS

FACTORY WASTE

What to Do Discuss with students what might happen if waste water from a chemical plant or factory gets into a grassy meadow. Help students trace the food chains that would be affected. One answer can be: chemicals enter soil, are absorbed by grass, which is eaten by cows, which are eaten by people, the cows and people could get ill, and the cows would have to be moved.

What's the Result? Encourage students to produce a diagram or a mobile to demonstrate how a chemical poison might travel through the food chain.

Materials Hints Paper clips may be used, in place of yarn, to connect the pictures. Use Activity Support Masters 1 and 2, TRB pp. 14–15.

Safety Review safety precautions with students.

2. Guide the Procedure

• Provide several old nature magazines, as well as art supplies.

• Suggest that students list the plant and the three animals horizontally and connect them with arrows to show that the plant is eaten by the first animal and the first animal is eaten by the second animal and so on. You might provide an example on the chalkboard for students to follow.

• **How are you part of a food chain?** Students might respond that they eat fruits, vegetables, and bread which come from plants, or that they eat meat from animals, such as cattle, which eat plants, such as clover.

Have students record their data and answer questions on *Science Notebook*, TRB, pp. 38–39.

Science Processor Have students use the CD-ROM Painter to draw their food chain.

3. Assess Performance

Process Skills Checklist

• Did students **make models** of food chains representing real-world relationships? Did the food chains show an animal eating a plant and a second animal eating the first animal?

• Were students able to accurately **classify** organisms as producers or consumers? Did they recognize that plants are producers and animals are consumers?

• Did students **infer** that producers begin food chains? Was a plant shown in the bottom-most picture of their food chain?

Analyze and Conclude

1. The producer should be the bottom picture of a plant.

2. The top three pictures of animals should be consumers.

3. Food chains begin with producers.

Activity More Links in the Food Chain

Preview *Students focus on linking food chains and find that a food web has many more links than a food chain.*

Advance Preparation *see p. E4b.*

1. Get Ready

 GROUPS OF 4–6

 45 MINUTES

Key Science Process Skills model, compare, infer, hypothesize, define operationally

Multi-Age Strategy Encourage advanced students to assemble more complex food webs, showing multiple food chains with numerous connections between them.

Materials Hints Pictures or drawings could be added to the index cards.

Safety Review safety precautions with students.

2. Guide the Procedure

- Students may prefer to tape the yarn to the cards.

 Math Hint *Assist any students who are having difficulty measuring out lengths of yarn. Remind students that the length is an estimate and does not have to be exact.*

- After students have completed their food webs, have them use their fingers to trace the separate food chains that make up the webs. You might have them count the total number of food chains that make up a food web.
- **Why do you think some food webs in nature are larger than others?** There are more kinds of plants and animals living in some places than in others, so the animals have more kinds of things to feed on.

 Have students record their data and answer questions on *Science Notebook*, TRB, pp. 40–41.

 Science Processor Have students use the CD-ROM Painter to draw their food webs.

Activity More Links in the Food Chain

MATERIALS
- index cards
- crayons or colored markers
- short lengths of blue yarn and red yarn
- scissors
- *Science Notebook*

Most living things eat more than one kind of food. Because they do, many food chains may be linked together. In this activity you will play a game to see how food chains can link to form food webs.

- -

Procedure

1. Work in a group to **write** the names of the following living things on index cards, one per card: berries, nuts, water plants, mouse, snake, big fish, small fish, crayfish, owl, bear, chipmunk.

2. Place all the cards face up. With your group, arrange some of the cards to form a food chain.

3. Place a piece of blue yarn, about 10 cm long, on top of two cards so that each end is on a card. Use additional lengths of blue yarn to connect the other cards in the food chain.

Step 3

 Math Hint *"About 10 cm" is an estimate. The length of yarn does not have to be exactly 10 cm.*

4. Use the remaining cards and blue yarn to create two more food chains.

5. Now **look** at the food chains you have made. **Find** a living thing in one food chain that can eat or be eaten by something in another food chain. Use a length of red yarn to connect these two cards.

E24

Meeting Individual Needs

STUDENTS ACQUIRING ENGLISH

Help students prepare labels with the words *producer* and *consumer*. Review with them the meaning of each word. Then direct students to use the labels to identify the producers and consumers in their food webs. You might also have students prepare and use labels to identify the herbivores, carnivores, omnivores, and decomposers in their food webs.

LINGUISTIC

Step 5

6. You have just linked two food chains together to form a food web. Find all the links between the food chains that you can. Connect the cards with lengths of red yarn. **Make a drawing** of your food web in your *Science Notebook*.

7. Look at the food webs made by other groups in your class. **Compare** these webs to the one your group made.

8. Think about what would happen if there were no producers. Take away the producer cards. **Infer** what would happen to the living things that eat the producers. **Infer** what would happen to the other members of the food web.

Analyze and Conclude

1. **Explain** how a food chain is different from a food web.

2. Suppose that most of the plants in a certain place die off. **Hypothesize** about what will happen to the animals that eat those plants.

UNIT PROJECT LINK

For this Unit Project you will make a mural of a tropical rain forest. Explore the producers of the different layers of the rain forest—the canopy, the understory, and the forest floor. With your classmates, make a mural showing different rain forest plants.

Technology Link

For more help with your Unit Project, go to **www.eduplace.com**.

E25

UNIT PROJECT LINK

Tropical rain forests have a great variety of plant life. Encourage students to find out about different types of producers—moss, small saplings, vines, flowers, and different trees of all sizes. Ask students to take notes on *Science Notebook*, TRB, p. 42. Then use Unit Project Masters 1 and 2 (TRB pp. 16–17) to research information on producers found in tropical rain forests.

TechnologyLink

Have students visit **www.eduplace.com** to link to content-related sites, and to locate agencies that can help with the Unit Project. You can also download Unit Project Masters, including a scoring rubric to assess students' progress.

• **If people hunt one animal so much that its population is greatly reduced, what else will be affected?** Students should realize that the other plants and animals in its food chain will be affected. For an example, discuss the case of wolves (See Science & Writing, p. E28). Farmers, ranchers, and hunters killed so many wolves that wolves became an endangered species. As a result, in many places deer populations increased to the point that there was not enough natural food for the deer, so the deer either starved or ate the crops. Today, wolves are being reintroduced in certain areas.

• **In some children's stories, such as *The Three Little Pigs*, and *Little Red Riding Hood*, the wolf is seen as being bad because the wolf is a carnivore. Do you think it is fair to treat carnivores as evil or bad?** Help students realize that carnivores are not bad creatures. They are necessary to keep populations of other creatures in check. Remind students that many carnivores are themselves hunted by other, bigger carnivores. If a carnivore is not hunted by other carnivores, its population is kept in check by the population of the creatures it eats. If the food supply for the wolves declines, then the wolf population will also decline.

3. Assess Performance

Process Skills Checklist

• Did students **make models** that show actual food web relationships? Were two or more food chains connected to each other in the food webs?

• Did students **infer** how food webs can change? Did they **infer** that a change in one part of a food web can cause changes in other parts of the food web?

Analyze and Conclude

1. A food chain links one living thing to another. A food web can link one living thing to several other living things. A food web is formed from two or more food chains.

2. Students should conclude that the animals would die off unless they could move to another place.

Who Eats Whom?

Reading Focus Have students look for *main ideas* as they read through the resource to help them answer the Reading Focus question.

1. Get Ready

Vocabulary
Science Terms food chain, predators, prey, food web
Support Term energy

Background
- When studying a long food chain, notice that at each higher level the consumers become fewer. This demonstrates what can be called the food or energy pyramid. At each level, the animals spend most of the energy they got from the level below on life activities—growing, repairing injuries, giving off heat to the atmosphere, reproducing. What they store in their bodies is all that's available for the next level of consumer. Ecologists have calculated that only about ten percent of the energy from one layer of the energy pyramid ever makes it to the next layer. In fact, they call it the ten-percent rule. The ten-percent rule explains why a field of grain can feed many more people directly (people eating grain) than it can indirectly (people eating beef cattle that ate grain).

Discussion Starter
- **What animals eat grasses?** Students might name cattle, horses, grasshoppers, zebras, antelopes, caribou, geese, lemmings, and others.

- **What animals eat grass eaters?** Students might name humans, cougars, lizards, lions, cheetahs, wolves, snakes, and others.

Who Eats Whom?

Reading Focus What is the difference between a food chain and a food web?

A FOOD CHAIN

Plant

Grasshopper

Lizard

A grasshopper clings to a plant in the bright sunlight and nibbles on a leaf. Suddenly a lizard darts up from behind. It shoots out its tongue and eats the grasshopper. As the lizard slips away through the grass, a snake strikes and swallows the lizard whole. Later, an owl catches the snake and flies off to feed it to her young.

Food Chains
Every living thing needs food because food provides energy. When one animal eats another animal or a plant, they both become part of a food chain. A **food chain** is the path that energy takes as one living thing eats another. In the example

above, the plant, grasshopper, lizard, snake, and owl are all connected to one another in a food chain. Cards are connected by yarn to show a food chain in the activity on pages E22 and E23. The plant, grasshopper, lizard, snake, and owl are all part of the same food chain.

Different environments, such as forests, deserts, or lakes, have different food chains. Some food chains are short, and some are long. But all food chains begin with a producer.

E26

Science & Writing

MAKING A MENU

What to Do Invite the class to pretend they are opening a restaurant called "Adventures in Food Chains." They must develop the menu. Divide the class into four groups with responsibility for developing one of the following sections of the menu: Soup/Salad, Appetizers, Main Courses, Desserts. Each item should appeal to one of the four kinds of consumers: herbivores, carnivores, omnivores, or decomposers.

What's the Result? Suggest students think of clever names for the dishes that would identify whether a dish is made from a producer, herbivore, carnivore, omnivore, or decomposer. Ask students to tell which consumer might like each dish. Encourage groups to illustrate their menus.

Links in the Chain

A plant is a producer and can make its own food. A producer is the first link in all food chains.

A consumer is the next link in a food chain. Animals are consumers. Some animals, such as grasshoppers, feed on plants. Then other animals, such as lizards, eat the animals that ate the plants.

Animals that hunt other animals for food are called **predators** (pred'ə tərz). The animals that are hunted by predators are called **prey**.

An animal can be both predator and prey. For example, a housefly may be eaten by a frog. In this case the frog is a predator. The fly is its prey. But the frog can become prey if a raccoon makes a meal of the frog.

▲ A frog can be predator and prey.

Likewise, the raccoon becomes prey if it's eaten by a predator, such as a cougar.

If no larger animal eats the cougar, does that mean the cougar is the top consumer in the chain? Not really. When the cougar dies, its body will become food for the last of the consumers—the decomposers. Bacteria, molds, and other decomposers feed on the remains of animals and break down these remains.

Snake

Owl

E27

Choose from the following strategies to facilitate discussion.

Making Inferences

• **Which animals in the food chain on pp. E26–E27 are predators?** The lizard, snake, and owl are predators. **Which are prey?** The grasshopper, lizard, and snake are prey. Point out that the same animal can be predator and prey.

Making Judgments

• **Why can't a consumer be the first link in a food chain?** A consumer cannot make its own food.

• **Can animals that eat plants be predators? Explain.** Animals that eat plants can be predators if they also eat other animals.

Connecting to the Activities

• *More Links in the Food Chain, pp. E24–E25*

• **Remember the food web you made. Who are the predators and prey in your food web?** Students should identify as prey any animal hunted and eaten by another animal, and as predator any animal that hunts and eats another animal. Producers (plants) are neither prey nor predators.

• **What animals in your food web are both predators and prey?** Any animal above the first consumer can be both predator and prey except any animal at the end of the chain.

Science & the Arts

DRAW A CARTOON

What to Do Discuss with students how some animals use their body parts to defend themselves against predators. For example, you might discuss how birds use their wings, frogs use their legs, snakes use their fangs, deer use their hooves, and porcupines use their sharp quills. Have students draw a two-frame cartoon showing a predator pouncing on a prey in the first frame and the prey escaping from or defending itself against the predator in the second frame.

What's the Result? Ask students to show their cartoons to the rest of the class, identify the predator and prey, and describe what is happening in each frame.

Caption answer: The snake and the hawk compete for the rabbit, and the rabbit and the grasshopper compete for the grass.

Thinking About the Data

- Point out that other arrows could have been drawn in this food web. Have students point out other possible relationships. For examples, herons eat bass, frogs, snakes, and probably grasshoppers too. Snakes also eat frogs and grasshoppers, and hawks also eat frogs. Animals that live in the same communities often compete for the same food. Ask: **What other things do animals compete for?** Students may know that animals compete for water, and for their territory and a place to live.

- **The student text calls decomposers "the last of the consumers." How is this both true and untrue?** Students might say that decomposers belong above the top predator of a food chain, so the term is appropriate in that sense. In another sense, decomposers make nutrients available for new producers to begin another food chain, so they aren't the end step at all but part of a cycle.

Transparencies 24 and 25: Visual/Spatial Activity

Use "Food Web" (base) and ask students to point out as many food chains as they can. Then use the overlay and have students compare it to their answers.

Drawing Conclusions

- **In the Arctic tundra live small mouselike animals called lemmings. In some years the lemming population is very large, but in other years lemmings are rare. How might the size of the lemming population affect these other inhabitants of the tundra: snowy owls, flowering plants, caribou, and hawks?** Students should conclude that a small lemming population will allow more flowering plants to survive for the caribou to eat, but it will also mean many snowy owls and hawks will starve. A large lemming population means the hawk and owl populations will grow but the flowering plant and caribou populations will suffer.

🎖 Meeting Individual Needs

Inclusion Have students diagram the food chain described in the text on pp. E26–E27. Ask them to label the predators and prey and point out which animals are both predators and prey. Use the students' diagrams to discuss the role of decomposers in food chains. Lead them to understand that decomposers feed on all the organisms in a food chain.

A FOOD WEB

Grass is eaten by a rabbit.

A rabbit is eaten by a hawk.

A rabbit is eaten by a snake.

A snake is eaten by a hawk.

▲ **What animals compete for the same food?**

Chains Tangle Into Webs

There are some simple food chains in nature. But usually two or more food chains overlap and link, forming a **food web**. A model of a food web is made in the activity on pages E24 and E25.

A forest food web might include an oak tree. When the oak tree drops its acorns, hungry squirrels may eat the acorns and collect some for winter. Deer, mice, shrews, bears, and raccoons also eat acorns.

But acorns are not the only food these animals eat. Deer also eat grass, leaves, moss, twigs and other plant parts. Mice also nibble on grass and eat insects and spiders.

E28

Science & Writing

LETTER WRITING

What to Do Over the years, ranchers in North America have killed many wolves to protect their livestock. Hunters also have killed wolves to protect animals that they hunt. As a result wolves are now an endangered species. Some deer populations have increased to the point where there is not enough food and many deer starve. Today, wolves are being reintroduced in some areas. Ranchers are allowed to kill a wolf only if they find it attacking their livestock. Discuss with students whether they think the killing of wolves should be prohibited.

What's the Result? Encourage students to write a letter to the U.S. Fish and Wildlife Service at the Department of the Interior, Washington, DC 20240 stating their views.

Grass is eaten by a grasshopper.

A grasshopper is eaten by a frog.

A frog is eaten by a bass.

A bass is eaten by a heron.

Small fish are eaten by a bass.

Raccoons also eat frogs, fish, fruit, crabs, grasshoppers, and sometimes even bird eggs.

You can see that in a large food web, many animals are connected to one another by the kinds of foods that they eat. Food webs show that every kind of living thing depends on other kinds of living things. Wherever you look in nature—in forests, lakes, meadows, oceans, or deserts—plants and animals are connected to one another through a web of life. ■

Internet Field Trip

Visit **www.eduplace.com** to learn about the food webs that spiders depend on for survival.

E29

Science & Literature

READING

What to Do *The Fall of Freddie the Leaf* by Leo Buscaglia, Ph.D. (Slack Inc., 1982), illustrates the life cycle of a leaf. Read this book and lead a discussion of how Freddie's seasonal life cycle compares with the cycle of food chains and webs of all living things. **Where would Freddie fit on the food chain?** Freddie and the tree of which he is part are producers. After Freddie dies, he would be acted on by decomposers. Nutrients from Freddie then would be used by other plants.

What's the Result? Have students draw a food chain that includes Freddie the leaf.

Making Comparisons

• **Do you think food webs are larger in a desert or in a tropical rain forest? Explain why.** Help students recognize that the food webs in a tropical rain forest would be larger because the rain forest has a greater variety of plants and animals than a desert does. As a result, there would be more connections between food chains.

Meeting Individual Needs

Students Acquiring English Group students who are proficient in English with students who are acquiring English. Provide students with name cards or pictures of plants and animals. Label the pictures, and encourage students to practice pronouncing the plant and animal names. Have students line up to form two or three separate food chains, keeping in mind what the animals on the cards eat. Direct students to place their right hand on the shoulder of the student preceding them in the food chain. Then have students try to form a food web by placing their left hand on the shoulder of a person in another food chain with an appropriate plant or animal card. Let each group of students develop a food web with as many of the pictured plants and animals as possible.

3. Assess Understanding

Students can work in groups of three or four. Invite each group to create the longest food chain it can and model it with pictures and yarn on the floor. Imaginary plants and animals are acceptable, but groups must give their predator/prey relationships. After the groups have presented their food chains, provide another color of yarn and have the groups begin to construct a food web using one or more of other groups' food chains.

Reading Focus Answer

A food chain is the path that energy takes as one living thing eats another. A food web is the overlapping and linking of two or more food chains.

Internet Field Trip

From **www.eduplace.com** students can link to a Web site about the role spiders play in food webs. A trip log will guide their visit to the site.

Cane Toads in Leaping Numbers

Reading Focus Have students look for *cause/effect* relationships as they read to answer the Reading Focus question. Remind them that sometimes they will <u>not</u> find words, such as *because, as a result,* and *so,* to help them.

1. Get Ready

Vocabulary
Science Term community

Background
* European settlers introduced many non-native animals to Australia, including horses, cattle, sheep, goats, pigs, deer, foxes, and rabbits. With few predators to control them, the population of wild rabbits exploded. The rabbits caused extensive damage to crops and grazing lands. A disease, myxomatosis, was deliberately introduced in an effort to wipe out the rabbits. The disease greatly reduced the rabbit population but did not solve the problem.

Discussion Starter
* If an animal is brought into a place where it has never lived before, what conditions would affect its survival? Encourage students to think about where the animal would fit into a new food chain. The animal must find food, not be easy prey for other animals, have enough water, perhaps find shelter, and so on.

2. Guide the Discussion

Choose from the following strategies to facilitate discussion.

 Students should see that the cane toad is as large or larger than their hand.

Identifying and Solving Problems
* **How might Australia solve its cane toad problem?** Students might suggest bringing in a cane toad predator, declaring a bounty on cane toads and their eggs, and making cane toad legs a gourmet food item.

Cane Toads in Leaping Numbers

Reading Focus How did cane toads change the food chains and food webs in Australia?

 Did you ever make a problem worse by trying to fix it? That's what happened in Australia in 1935. At that time, scientists thought they had discovered a way to get rid of the insects that were eating their crops. The result of their action was a country covered with huge toads, called cane toads. Cane toads may be as much as 23 cm (9 in.) long!

Cane toads live in Hawaii and other parts of the tropics. In 1935, scientists brought a group of cane toads to Australia to eat the beetles that were destroying the sugar cane crops. The scientists' idea might have worked except for one problem. The beetles' habitat is inside the sugar cane plants, but the toads' habitat is on the ground. Their paths never crossed, so the toads never ate the beetles.

This cane toad shown is life-size. How does the size of this cane toad compare with the size of your hand?

E30

Science & Social Studies

FLORIDA EVERGLADES
What to Do Discuss how the Florida Everglades became an unstable environment in the 20th century, due in part to the introduction of non-native plants and animals. For example, in the 1950s an aquarium plant called Florida elodea entered the Everglades water system. Now it clogs the waterways. In 1963 scientists introduced the grass carp from Asia to control the elodea. However, grass carp eat almost all water plants, so wherever the carp are, other water herbivores go hungry.
What's the Result? Encourage students to do research and write a paragraph describing how people affected the Everglades.

Although the cane toads didn't solve the beetle problem, they did make a difference. The toads changed the natural community (kə myoō'nə tē). A **community** is a group of plants and animals that live in the same area and depend on one another. When an animal is added to or taken away from a community, the food chains and food webs change.

The cane toads became part of the food chains and food webs in their new home. The huge toads gobbled up many of Australia's native lizards, snakes, mice, and birds. Scientists became worried about the possible extinction of these native animals.

The toad problem quickly became worse. Cane toads were laying up to 20,000 eggs at a time. And the toads had no natural predators. That's because the toads can protect themselves from being eaten by releasing poison from their necks. The native animals that tried to eat them were often poisoned to death!

In spite of the trouble they've caused, cane toads have become part of the culture in Australia. Some people consider them a tourist attraction. One politician even suggested putting up a statue to honor the cane toad! What do you think? Is Australia's cane toad a pet or a pest? ∎

Science in Literature

One Small Square: African Savanna
by Donald M. Silver
Illustrated by
Patricia J. Wynne and Dianne Ettl
W. H. Freeman & Co., 1994

GRASS EATERS RUN FOR LIFE!

"The African savanna is home to the biggest, the tallest, and the fastest land animals on earth. It is where killer dogs work together as a team, and tiny termites build nests as high as the ceiling in your room and as hard as cement. One minute all is calm. The next, there is panic as thousands of grass eaters run for their lives."

More interesting facts can be found in the book *One Small Square: African Savanna* by Donald M. Silver. Enjoy fun activities while you explore life in the dangerous savanna.

E31

Science & Writing

FLOW CHARTS
What to Do? Help students make a simple flow chart that summarizes what happened to the beetles, sugar cane, lizards, snakes, and other small animals in Australia when the cane toad was introduced in the 1930s. What might have happened to food webs in Australia if the cane toad had caused many small animals to become extinct? There might not have been enough food for the large animals in the food web that fed on those small animals. As a result, the large animals might also have died.

What's the Result? Students' flow charts should show a series of events. The flow chart might include sentences such as *Beetles eat the sugar cane and cane toads are brought to Australia.*

- **What might go wrong with each solution?** The cane toad predators might cause more trouble than they solve. The cane toad population might grow more quickly than bounty hunters could reduce it, and the bounty might cost the government a lot of money.

- **How could researchers avoid these problems?** Students might suggest testing each idea on a small scale before making any final decisions.

Connecting to the Activities
- *More Links in the Food Chain, pp. E24–E25*
- **Where might the cane toad fit in the food web you made?** Students should recognize that the cane toad is a carnivore and so would fit in the food web at some point after the herbivores.

 Meeting Individual Needs
Students Acquiring English Find pictures of different communities and extinct animals to help students visualize these key terms in the reading. You may have to help students distinguish between a pet and a pest.

 ## Science in Literature

One Small Square: African Savanna
by Donald M. Silver
After students have read pp. 8–23 to find out who eats whom on the African savanna, they can work in small groups to draw a food web. Remind them to include plants and decomposers.

Science Processor Suggest students use the CD-ROM Painter to draw their food webs.

3. Assess Understanding

 Have students pretend they are members of a town council. Conduct a town meeting discussing the merits and problems of increasing the cat population to help control a rat problem.

Reading Focus Answer

The cane toads became part of the native food chains and webs, eating lizards, snakes, mice, and birds to the point of near extinction. Since they had no natural predators, the toads increased greatly in number and their poison killed those few predators that tried to eat them.

Deadly Links

RESOURCE

Reading Focus As students read the section headed "Pelican Problems" on page E33, have them look for *cause/effect* relationships to answer the Reading Focus question.

1. Get Ready

Vocabulary
Support Terms insecticides, DDT

Background
- Following World War II, a wide range of pesticides and insecticides, including DDT, was introduced to wipe out pests and improve crop yields. Not until 1962, when Rachel Carson's book *Silent Spring* was published, did people become aware of the damage these insecticides were doing. Carson pointed out that the insecticides were concentrating in the bodies of consumers in the food chain and warned that there might come a time when there would be no more birds. Her efforts helped lead to the restriction of insecticide use in the United States and other parts of the world.

Discussion Starter
- **Some fruits and vegetables are labeled "organically grown" and sold in health-food stores. In what ways are these foods different?** Organically grown food is not sprayed with chemicals or insecticides. Explain that insecticides are sprayed on produce to protect it from insects. Tests show that these substances should not be harmful to humans.

2. Guide the Discussion

Choose from the following strategies to facilitate discussion.

Making Inferences
- **Suppose you're spraying an insecticide in your backyard. What do you think happens to the insecticide?** Students should infer that much of the insecticide may be blown to other places, settle on the plants and other objects, or get washed into the soil.

Deadly Links

RESOURCE

Reading Focus What caused the brown pelican to become endangered?

 Suppose insects were destroying tomato plants you were growing. What would you do? You might spray an insecticide (in sek'tə sīd) on the plants to kill the insects. Insecticides are chemicals used to destroy insects that harm plants or carry diseases.

Killing Pests
Insecticides have been used widely throughout the world. Insecticides can help farmers keep crops growing healthy and strong. But these chemicals may remain in the soil for years. Some insecticides sprayed before you were born may still be in the soil today!

▲ **Insecticides can help crops grow.**

E32

Through research, scientists found out that insecticides can harm more than the pests they were made to kill. The poisonous chemicals can be carried off by wind and moving water to new places. Once in these new places, the chemicals can harm wildlife. This was the case with DDT, an insecticide. DDT can kill many kinds of flies and mosquitoes that carry diseases. Even though DDT was useful for killing pests, it had harmful effects on other animals, such as the bald eagle and the brown pelican.

Science, Technology & Society

INTERVIEWING

What to Do Many home gardeners spread their gardens with large amounts of insecticides, herbicides, and chemical fertilizers. When it rains, the excess washes into rivers. There the extra nitrogen and phosphorus cause an algae "bloom." Dead algae drifting to the bottom makes the decomposers work harder than before. This process uses up a lot of oxygen. Fish can suffocate in an algae bloom. Help interested students formulate several questions to ask a family member or a neighbor who gardens. Have them find out about the kinds of insecticides, herbicides, and fertilizers people use.

What's the Result? Have students share their findings with the class.

Follow the path of chemicals through this food chain. The addition of chemicals can cause changes in food chains, too. ▼

Pelican Problems

In California, DDT came close to killing all of the state's brown pelicans during the 1960s and 1970s. Scientists found that DDT from a factory was carried off in the waste water from the plant. Some of this waste water ended up in ocean waters. There the DDT was taken in by fish. When the brown pelicans ate these fish, the birds took DDT into their own bodies.

As DDT moves along a food chain, it is stored in the bodies of animals for a long time. When the brown pelicans laid their eggs, the DDT stored in the parent birds' bodies caused most eggs to have very thin shells. Most shells broke before the baby pelicans could grow. Because of DDT, there were hardly any new baby brown pelicans during those years. So the number of brown pelicans greatly decreased.

Brown pelicans on the East Coast and in Louisiana were also being harmed by DDT. In Louisiana the brown pelican had been named the state bird back when there were close to 100,000 pelicans in the state. Because of DDT, pelicans in Louisiana disappeared completely!

E33

Science Around the World

SAVING NATURE

What to Do Briefly describe the work of Maria Tereza Jorge Padua. As president of Funatura, a Brazilian conservation foundation, she has established national parks and reserves that today protect millions of acres and many waterways from developers. She is also an expert on the effect of herbicides on land and animals. Some of her critics complain that she is not interested in helping the native people make a living. Encourage students to write questions they might ask Jorge Padua about her work.

What's the Result? Why is it sometimes difficult to balance the needs of nature with the needs of people? Students may say the needs of people sometimes seem to require harming nature.

Drawing Conclusions

- **What might the scientists who recommended DDT in the 1940s have done to see whether it was safe?** Students may suggest lab tests to study the effect of DDT on members of several food chains.

Connecting to the Activities

- *More Links in the Food Chain, pp. E24–E25*
- **How might DDT move through the food web you made?** If DDT were sprayed on the producers in the food web, it would then pass to the herbivores that ate them. Then it would pass to the carnivores that fed on the herbivores.

Thinking Critically

- **Imagine that mercury was polluting Earth's oceans. If mercury, like DDT, is stored in fat tissue, which ocean-dwelling animals would be likely to have poisonous amounts of mercury stored in their bodies?** Animals at the top of a food chain, such as sharks, tuna, dolphins, porpoises, and so on, would have toxic levels of mercury.

Meeting Individual Needs

For Extra Help At home, poke two small holes into a raw egg, one at each end. Blow the contents through the eggshell. Rinse the eggshell and let it dry. Allow students to gently touch and handle it. Ask: **How would you describe the eggshell?** The eggshell is thin and light-weight. Help students recall that DDT caused pelican eggshells to become thinner than normal and to break easily. **What might have caused the pelican eggshells to break?** Students might mention bumping into other objects or the female pelican sitting on the eggs. You might have a student demonstrate how easily the empty eggshell is broken with a slight squeeze.

3. Assess Understanding

Have students work in groups of three or four. Have each group play the role of a different kind of farmer. Ask them if they would use agricultural chemicals for their crops or in feed for their animals and report to the class on their decisions.

Reading Focus Answer

Brown pelicans became endangered due to the introduction of DDT to the pelican's food chain and its weakening effect on the pelicans' eggshells.

Close
the Investigation

INVESTIGATION WRAP-UP

REVIEW

1. Students should indicate that a food web is made up of two or more food chains that overlap and link.

2. Students' answers should indicate an understanding that almost all predators are prey to other predators in a food chain or food web.

CRITICAL THINKING

3. Students' drawings should reveal a clear understanding of the concepts of food chains and food webs. *(Analyzing, Applying, Expressing Ideas)*

4. Accept all reasonable answers. Answers should reflect an understanding that affecting one member of a food chain or food web will also affect other members. *(Evaluating, Expressing Ideas)*

CHALLENGE

Encourage students to imagine what happens to a forest during a fire. Ask them to describe orally or in writing what would happen to a forest food web if most of the vegetation had been burned. Have them suggest how this would affect food webs in neighboring areas. Students should note that if predators from one area are pushed into another area, this puts pressure on existing food webs. There may not be enough food for all predators.

FOLLOWING UP

Baseline Assessment Refer to the class list of responses regarding herbivores and carnivores. For each herbivore listed, identify a carnivore that preys on it. For each carnivore listed, identify another living thing that it preys on and, if there is one, an animal for which it is prey.

Reteaching Have students create a collage or bulletin board using words and pictures from old nature magazines that show feeding relationships among living things in food webs.

Use *Science Notebook,* TRB p. 43.

▲ DDT caused brown pelicans to lay eggs with very thin shells.

The Start of a Solution

In 1970 the pelican was listed as endangered. Something had to be done, or there would be no brown pelicans left. Finally, DDT was banned in the United States in 1972. Since then the number of pelicans has been on the rise.

Pelicans were not the only birds that were harmed by DDT. Bald eagles and peregrine falcons also laid eggs with thin shells because of the DDT stored in their bodies.

The law preventing the use of DDT has helped each of these great birds recover from the harmful chemical. But other countries still use DDT.

Although the use of DDT has been banned in the United States, there is still a need for insecticides. Today farmers use safer chemicals in smaller amounts. This means there is far less harm to the environment than with the use of DDT. ■

——— INVESTIGATION 3 WRAP-UP ———

REVIEW **1.** What is the difference between a food chain and a food web?

2. Can an animal be a predator and also prey? Explain your answer.

CRITICAL THINKING **3.** Think about the different things you eat and where they come from. Draw a diagram that shows you as part of a food web.

4. You see a sign that says, "Our new insecticide kills all bugs!" Do you think buying this product is a good idea or a bad idea? Explain your answer.

E34

Assessment

Investigation Review

Name _____ Date _____

Use the names of the living things in the box to fill in the rectangles that make a food chain. Then answer the questions below.

| frog | snake | insect | leaf |

| leaf | insect | frog | snake |

1. Which animals in the food chain are prey? insect, frog
2. Which animals are predators? frog, snake
3. Look at the drawing below. Draw an arrow from each living thing to the living thing that eats it. Then answer the question below.

4. Which living things in the drawing above compete for the same food? Write your answers on a separate sheet of paper.
The deer, mouse, and rabbit all compete for vegetation. The owl and the fox compete for the mouse and the rabbit.

Process Skills *Making a Model* If cane toads, insects, and sugar cane plants had been placed together in an enclosed area How might making a model have helped prevent the cane that simulated the toad problem in Australia? Write your answer on a separate actual conditions sheet of paper. of the Australian sugar cane fields, observers may have realized that the toads would not be able to eat the insects.

Portfolio

Make a Sequence Chain
Have students make a diagram that shows the sequence of events that led up to the endangerment of the brown pelican. Diagrams might begin with the phrase *DDT used to kill insects* and end with *brown pelican endangered.* Use the Activity Support Master "Sequence Chart" on TRB p. 11.

◄ **Investigation Review**
Use Investigation Review p. 109 in the *Teacher Resource Book.*

REFLECT & EVALUATE

Word Power

Write the letter of the term that best matches the definition. *Not all terms will be used.*

1. Path that energy takes as one thing eats another
2. Animal that eats plants and other animals
3. Living things that make their own food
4. Everything that surrounds and affects a living thing
5. Animal that hunts another animal for food
6. Place where an animal lives

a. carnivore
b. environment
c. food chain
d. food web
e. habitat
f. omnivore
g. predator
h. producers

Check What You Know

Write the term in each pair that best completes each sentence.

1. Bacteria, mushrooms, and molds are (producers, decomposers).
2. Two food chains that overlap form (a food web, an environment).
3. A living thing that eats plants, animals, or other living things is (a consumer, a predator).
4. Animals that are hunted are (predators, prey).

Problem Solving

1. Some animals are herbivores, others are carnivores, and still others are omnivores. Which are you? How do you know? Use the definitions of all three terms in your answer.

2. Suppose a tree near your home dies. Explain how this may cause changes in a food chain.

BUILD YOUR PORTFOLIO

Study the drawings. Explain how a frog can be both predator and prey.

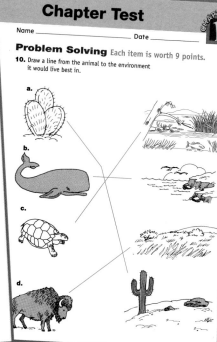

E35

Assessment

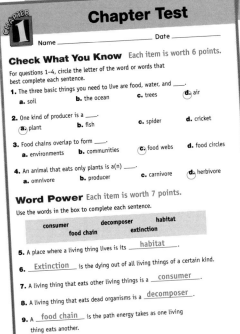

Chapter Test

Name _____ Date _____

Check What You Know Each item is worth 6 points.

For questions 1–4, circle the letter of the word or words that best complete each sentence.

1. The three basic things you need to live are food, water, and ___.
   a. soil   b. the ocean   c. trees   d. air

2. One kind of producer is a ___.
   a. plant   b. fish   c. spider   d. cricket

3. Food chains overlap to form ___.
   a. environments   b. communities   c. food webs   d. food circles

4. An animal that eats only plants is a(n) ___.
   a. omnivore   b. producer   c. carnivore   d. herbivore

Word Power Each item is worth 7 points.

Use the words in the box to complete each sentence.

| consumer | decomposer | habitat |
| food chain | | extinction |

5. A place where a living thing lives is its __habitat__.

6. __Extinction__ is the dying out of all living things of a certain kind.

7. A living thing that eats other living things is a __consumer__.

8. A living thing that eats dead organisms is a __decomposer__.

9. A __food chain__ is the path energy takes as one living thing eats another.

Chapter Test

Name _____ Date _____

Problem Solving Each item is worth 9 points.

10. Draw a line from the animal to the environment it would live best in.

a.
b.
c.
d.

REFLECT & EVALUATE

Word Power

1. c   **2.** f   **3.** h   **4.** b   **5.** g   **6.** e

Check What You Know

1. decomposers   **2.** food web   **3.** consumer   **4.** prey

Problem Solving

1. Most students are omnivores because they eat both meat and plants. Some might be herbivores because they eat only plants. Few, if any, people are carnivores, who eat only meat.

2. Answers should reflect an understanding that a tree is not only a producer but also provides a habitat for many species. The loss of one tree could affect the food supply and/or habitats for many species in a food chain. But now the tree is food for the decomposers.

BUILD YOUR PORTFOLIO

Students should indicate that the frog is predator to the insect and prey of the raccoon.

Assess Performance

Student Task

Have students make a poster showing a food chain for a city park or a forest. Students should include at least four living things in the food chain.

Scoring Rubric

Points	What To Look For
3	Student's poster clearly illustrates the definition of a food chain.
2	Student's poster is generally logical but some aspects are not accurate or shown clearly.
1	The poster is unclear, illogical, and includes fewer than four living things.

◀ **Chapter Test**

Use pp. 110–111 in the *Teacher Resource Book*.

ADAPTATIONS OF LIVING THINGS

Subconcepts	Activities	Materials
Investigation 1 How Are Living Things Adapted for Getting Food? pp. E38–E45		
Living things vary in their adaptations for getting food. *Suggested Pacing: 2-3 class periods* **Project 2061 Benchmarks** See page E 1c, number 2.	**The Right Beak for the Job,** p. E38 *Science Process Skills:* observe; measure/use numbers; infer; predict; collect, record, and interpret data; identify and control variables; make hypotheses; make and use models	**The Right Beak for the Job** goggles*, rectangular pan*, sand*, water, raisins, uncooked rice, plastic straw*, scissors, toothpick*, plastic fork* with tape on tines, plastic soup spoon*, *Science Notebook,* TRB pp. 49–50
Investigation 2 How Are Living Things Adapted for Protection? pp. E46–E56		
Living things vary in their adaptations for protection, including repellent body parts or chemicals, mimicking dangerous creatures, defensive behaviors, and camouflage. *Suggested Pacing: 3–4 class periods* **Project 2061 Benchmarks** See page E 1c, number 2.	**Blending In,** p. E46 *Science Process Skills:* predict, make hypotheses, make and use models	**Blending In** colored paper, colored markers, colored pencils or crayons, scissors, tape, *Science Notebook,* TRB pp. 53–54

E 36a CHAPTER 2

Overview
In this chapter students investigate how living things are adapted for getting food and protection.

Chapter Concept
Living things have structural and behavioral adaptations that allow them to survive in their environments.

Theme: Constancy and Change
Living things adapt to a specific environment over a long period of time and many generations. If the environment changes, living things must also change to survive or they must find a new environment.

Advance Preparation	Resources/Vocabulary	Assessment
The Right Beak for the Job None	**Catching Lunch** **Vocabulary:** adaptations, behavior, nutrient **A Quick Tongue** **Vocabulary:** camouflage	**Chapter 2 Baseline Assessment:** TRB pp. 47–48 **Investigation 1 Baseline Assessment:** TG p. E38 **Investigation 1 Review:** TRB p. 113 **Think It/Write It:** p. E45 TRB p. 52 **Following Up on Baseline Assessment:** TG p. E45 **Portfolio:** TG p. E45
Blending In None	**Hiding Out and Other Defenses** **Vocabulary:** parasite **Medicines from Nature**	**Investigation 2 Baseline Assessment:** TG p. E46 **Investigation 2 Review:** TRB p.114 **Think It/Write It:** p. E56 TRB p. 56 **Following Up on Baseline Assessment:** TG p. E56 **Performance:** TG p. E56 **Chapter 2 Summative Assessment:** Reflect and Evaluate: p. E57 Chapter 2 Review/Test: TRB pp. 115–116 *Science Notebook,* TRB pp. 57–58

*Materials in the Equipment Kit	TG= Teaching Guide	TRB= Teacher Resource Book

Chapter Overview

Concept Preview

You may wish to use Transparency E2 to introduce some of the important concepts of the chapter. Students can add to the map as they complete each Activity and Resource. Then they can use the completed map as a study guide.

Vocabulary Development

You may use Vocabulary Master E2 at any point in the chapter for additional vocabulary support.

Common Misconceptions

Students may think that one adaptation is "better" than another. Emphasize that the "best" adaptation for an animal is the one that helps it to survive.

Introducing the Chapter

Warm-Up Activity

 Have groups of students choose an animal and imagine that they must try to live like that animal for a day, even though they still have the body of a human being. How, for example, would they get up into a nest if they can't fly? Groups should discuss the challenges they would face in getting food and trying to defend themselves from predators.

Use *Science Notebook*, TRB pp. 47–48.

Discussion Starter

Initiate a discussion about students' current understanding of animals and their senses.

- **What animal senses are better than humans' and which senses are worse than humans'?** Answers might include eyesight, hearing and sense of smell.

ADAPTATIONS OF LIVING THINGS

To survive, or stay alive, plants and animals need to have food. They need to protect themselves from danger, too. How could a good sense of hearing help an animal get food? What part of a plant could stop a hungry animal from eating it?

PEOPLE USING SCIENCE

Aquarium Curator Would you like to give a 200-pound harbor seal a dental exam? That's one of the jobs that Rhona St. Clair-Moore did while working at the Thomas H. Kean New Jersey State Aquarium where she headed the marine mammal program. She was also the first woman to be named curator (kyoo rāt'ər) at the aquarium. A curator is a person in charge of a section of a museum, library, or aquarium.

Rhona St. Clair-Moore says she has always liked animals. "When I was young, I watched nature shows with my father. I asked questions about animals." Her interest led her to follow a career at the aquarium.

In this chapter you'll read how many kinds of living things survive in their environment.

E36

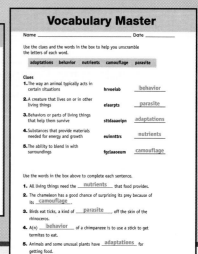

Concept Preview

Transparency

Plants and animals have adaptations for survival.

For Protection — For Food

Plant example: Rosebushes have thorns, which prevent animals from eating them.

Animal example: Camouflage helps a katydid hide from its predators.

Plant example: A Venus' flytrap traps insects with its leaves.

Animal example: A chameleon has a sticky tongue to catch insects.

▲ **Reading Support Book**
Transparency E2

Vocabulary Development

Vocabulary Master

Name _____ Date _____

Use the clues and the words in the box to help you unscramble the letters of each word.

| adaptations | behavior | nutrients | camouflage | parasite |

Clues

1. The way an animal typically acts in certain situations — hrvoelab — **behavior**

2. A creature that lives on or in other living things — elaarpts — **parasite**

3. Behaviors or parts of living things that help them survive — sttdaaaolpn — **adaptations**

4. Substances that provide materials needed for energy and growth — euinnttrs — **nutrients**

5. The ability to blend in with surroundings — fgclaaoeum — **camouflage**

Use the words in the box above to complete each sentence.

1. All living things need the _**nutrients**_ that food provides.

2. The chameleon has a good chance of surprising its prey because of its _**camouflage**_.

3. Birds eat ticks, a kind of _**parasite**_, off the skin of the rhinoceros.

4. A(n) _**behavior**_ of a chimpanzee is to use a stick to get termites to eat.

5. Animals and some unusual plants have _**adaptations**_ for getting food.

▲ **Reading Support Book**
Vocabulary Master E2

Coming Up

INVESTIGATION 1

HOW ARE LIVING THINGS ADAPTED FOR GETTING FOOD?
. . . . E38

INVESTIGATION 2

HOW ARE LIVING THINGS ADAPTED FOR PROTECTION?
. . . . E46

Rhona St. Clair-Moore blows a whistle when a seal is rewarded with food for good behavior. ▼

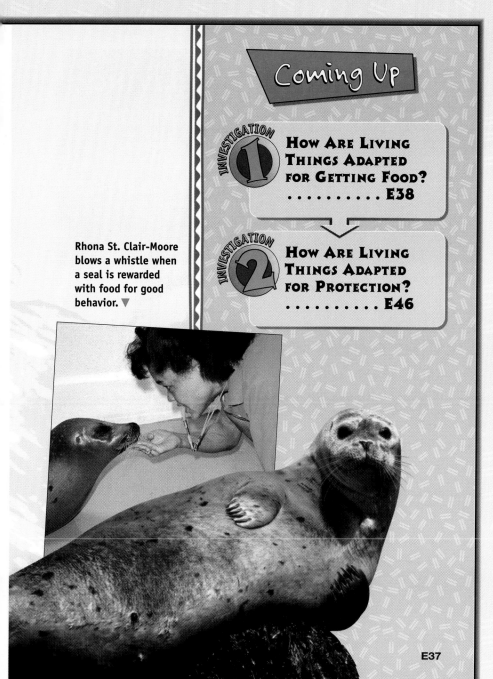

E37

Chapter Road Map

INVESTIGATION 1

HOW ARE LIVING THINGS ADAPTED FOR GETTING FOOD?

Activities	Resources
✷ The Right Beak for the Job	✷ Catching Lunch A Quick Tongue

INVESTIGATION 2

HOW ARE LIVING THINGS ADAPTED FOR PROTECTION?

Activities	Resources
✷ Blending In	✷ Hiding Out and Other Defenses Medicines From Nature

✷ Pressed for Time?

If you are pressed for time, focus on the Activities and Resources identified by this clock.

Home-School Connection

Distribute the Explore at Home Activity "Fingers and Toes" (Teacher Resource Book, page 4) to students after they have completed the chapter.

Technology Link

Videotape

Bill Nye the Science Guy *Plants*
Bill shows how various plants play defense, putting energy into defensive adaptations that help them survive. In another segment, the "Way Cool Scientist" studies plants for their medicinal value, explaining how chemicals in the leaves of rain forest plants could lead to the discovery of potential new medicines. Later, Bill illustrates how carnivorous plants have found a way to get additional nutrients. (Disney Educational Productions 1-800-295-5010)

Correlation to AIMS

If you use AIMS Activities, you may wish to use the Activity "Hide 'n Seek" on pages 120–123 in the *Critters* book to further explore how living things adapt for protection.

Start
the Investigation

HOW ARE LIVING THINGS ADAPTED FOR GETTING FOOD?

pages E38–E45

Planner

Subconcept Living things vary in their adaptations for getting food.

Objectives

- **Compare** the parts of living things and show how they are adapted for a certain environment.
- **Evaluate** the behaviors of living things that suit an organism to a particular lifestyle.

Pacing 2–3 class periods

Science Terms adaptation, behavior, nutrient, camouflage

Activate Prior Knowledge

Baseline Assessment Ask: **What kinds of animals have you observed collecting and eating food?** Save responses for use in Following Up.

HOW ARE LIVING THINGS ADAPTED FOR GETTING FOOD?

A big eagle swoops down from the sky. It grabs a fish out of the water and flies away. How are eagles adapted to catch, carry, and eat fish? In Investigation 1 you'll explore many adaptations living things have for getting food.

Activity

The Right Beak for the Job

Why do birds have different kinds of beaks? How does a beak's shape help birds get food?

MATERIALS
- goggles
- rectangular pan
- sand
- water
- raisins
- uncooked rice
- plastic straw
- scissors
- toothpick
- plastic fork with tape on tines
- plastic soup spoon
- *Science Notebook*

SAFETY

Do not eat any raisins or rice. Wear goggles during this activity.

Procedure

1. Set up a pan with sand, as shown. Add water to the pan until it is two-thirds full.

2. Bury six to ten raisins in the sand. Sprinkle rice in the shallow water where the sand begins to slope upward.

3. Cut a plastic straw into five pieces. Place the pieces in the water so that they float.

 Step 1

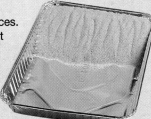

E38

Activity

The Right Beak for the Job

Preview *Students examine three kinds of bird beaks and how birds use their beaks to get food.*

1. Get Ready

 GROUPS OF 4–6   **45 MINUTES**

Key Science Process Skills make models, predict, observe, record, hypothesize, infer

Materials Hints Each group will need enough sand to fill $\frac{1}{3}$ of the pan, enough water to fill $\frac{2}{3}$ of the pan, 6–10 raisins, and about $\frac{1}{4}$ cup of uncooked rice.

Meeting Individual Needs

INCLUSION

Show students pictures of birds with beaks like those modeled in the activity. (toothpick—egrets, herons, sandpipers; fork—ducks; spoon—pelicans, puffins, storks) Encourage them to match the birds with the beaks in the activity.

VISUAL/SPATIAL

4. The raisins are models of small animals that live buried in the sand. The rice grains are small plants and animals that live in shallow water. The pieces of straw are models for fish. A toothpick, a plastic fork with taped tines, and a plastic soup spoon represent different kinds of bird beaks. In your *Science Notebook,* predict which beak is best for getting each kind of food.

Step 5

5. Make a chart like the one shown. Use the toothpick to find and pick up raisins in the sand. Count the number of raisins you pick up in ten tries. Record this number in your chart. Now use the toothpick to pick up rice and then pieces of the straw. Record all your results in your chart.

Kind of "Beak"	Number of Raisins	Number of Rice Grains	Number of Straw Pieces
toothpick			
fork			
spoon			

6. Replace the raisins, rice, and straw pieces. Repeat step 5, using the fork and then the spoon. Describe the methods you used with the different beaks and the different kinds of foods.

Analyze and Conclude

1. Which beak was best for collecting which food?

2. Think about the birds that would catch the plants and animals described in step 4. Hypothesize what each one's beak would look like. How is each bird's beak better than the models that you made?

3. Infer what birds with similar kinds of beaks have in common.

E39

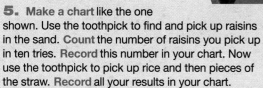

Technology Link CD-ROM

INVESTIGATE FURTHER!

Use the **Best of the Net—Science CD-ROM**, Life Sciences, *Miocene Sharks' Teeth of Calvert County* to learn more interesting facts about sharks. You'll find out about the many shark fossils dating back millions of years that geologists have found. And you'll learn how well sharks are adapted to their watery environment.

Technology Link CD-ROM

INVESTIGATE FURTHER!

Students can use the **Best of the Net—Science CD-ROM** Life Sciences, *Miocene Sharks' Teeth of Calvert County* to investigate more about sharks. At the *Miocene Sharks' Teeth* site, students learn about the history of sharks in the Calvert County, Maryland area. They learn why there are many whale bones in this area and discover how geological changes of the past have left shark teeth high in the cliffs above the water. Students can complete an activity in which they answer questions about what they learned.

Safety Review safety precautions with students. Caution students not to eat anything used in the activity.

2. Guide the Procedure

- **In what types of habitats would you expect to find birds living?** They live in environments all over the world including woodlands, cities, rain forests, marshes, grasslands, deserts, mountains, wetlands, sea coasts, and even near the poles. **Why can different birds live in such a wide variety of places?** Lead students to conclude that different birds eat different food and use different methods of feeding.

- **What different foods can you think of that birds eat?** Possible answers include fruits, berries, worms, insects, fish, water plants, seeds, grain, and mice.

- **What body parts do birds use to locate and obtain their food?** Answers should include eyes, beaks, feet, and wings.

 Have students record their predictions and findings on *Science Notebook,* TRB, pp. 49–50.

3. Assess Performance

Process Skills Checklist

- Did students base their predictions on reasoning rather than guessing?
- Did students make careful observations and accurately record data about the number of objects picked up?
- Did students make reasonable hypotheses about the shapes of birds' beaks and did they infer that birds with similar beaks eat similar foods?

Analyze and Conclude

1. Students should find that the toothpick is best for picking up the raisins, the fork with tape is best for picking up the pieces of rice, and the spoon is best for picking up the pieces of straws.

2. Students should hypothesize that a bird that catches small animals buried in the mud or sand would have a pointy beak. Students should understand that for trapping small animals in shallow waters, a beak could be adapted to resemble a strainer. Students should hypothesize that for catching fish in the deep ocean waters, a large, rounded beak that is used as a scoop would work best.

3. Students should infer that birds with similar beaks eat the same types of food.

Catching Lunch

Catching Lunch

Reading Focus Restate the Reading Focus question as a **main idea:** Adaptations help living things get food. Ask students to read to find important **details** that support the main idea and form a response to the question.

1. Get Ready

Vocabulary
Science Terms adaptations, behavior, nutrient

Support Terms survive, kilometer, poisonous, nectar, meter

Background

• The word *adaptation* refers to any characteristic of an organism that promotes its survival and ability to reproduce in its environment. Different species have different adaptations; also, no two individuals of the same species are exactly alike.

• Individual organisms in nature produce more off-spring than can survive; those that have variations better adapted to their environment have a better chance of surviving and reproducing. This process is called natural selection.

Discussion Starter

• **Have you ever seen birds, squirrels, or other animals in the woods or in a park searching for food and eating it? How do they search? How do they eat?** Encourage students to describe in words and demonstrate in actions how birds and squirrels move about to find food and how they eat.

Reading Focus How do adaptations help living things get food?

When you say "I'm starved!" does someone make you a sandwich or snack? Animals in nature must find food in order to get a meal. Their task is made a little easier by the adaptations (ad əp tā'shənz) they have. **Adaptations** are behaviors or parts of living things that help the living things survive in a certain environment. Animals have adaptations for getting food. And so do some unusual plants.

It Makes Good Sense

Animals have special body parts that help them get food. Many animals have extraordinary vision, a super sense of hearing, or a sharp

This snake injects poison. ▼

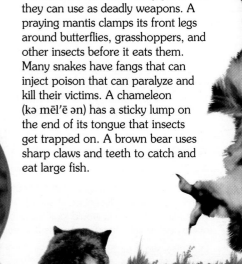

E40

sense of smell that helps them get food. Hunting birds, such as eagles and hawks, have very good eyes. They can spot prey from over a kilometer (half a mile) away! A dog's keen sense of smell can help uncover a tasty bone buried last year. The dog follows a scent trail that you couldn't smell at all! An owl, hunting at night, is able to swoop down on a mouse it can see running in the dark.

Deadly Weapons

Animals often have body parts that they can use as deadly weapons. A praying mantis clamps its front legs around butterflies, grasshoppers, and other insects before it eats them. Many snakes have fangs that can inject poison that can paralyze and kill their victims. A chameleon (kə mēl'ē ən) has a sticky lump on the end of its tongue that insects get trapped on. A brown bear uses sharp claws and teeth to catch and eat large fish.

Science, Technology & Society

ADAPTATION

What to Do Although humans are well adapted to certain habitats, without technological advances we wouldn't be able to live in many of the places we do. Everything from clothing and medicine to shelters and agriculture enables us to live where we could not otherwise survive. People have even lived for long periods in space. While technological advances are not really adaptations, the ability to develop them is an adaptation. Students can see how much they depend on technology by making a list of all of the manufactured products they use.

What's the Result? Students can summarize their results by making collages of such manufactured items that are necessary for survival.

A Handy Tool!

The activity about bird beaks on pages E38 and E39 shows that some beaks are better for catching certain kinds of foods than other beaks. Woodpeckers use their pointed beaks to drill into trees so that they can catch insects.

An owl catches a deer mouse. ▼

Hummingbirds have long beaks and tongues that they use for sipping nectar from flowers.

Using Math *You can make your own nectar for hummingbirds by mixing 1 part sugar to 4 parts water. How many cups of sugar would you use with 8 cups of water?*

E41

Science & Writing

USING VERBS

What to Do As students read *Catching Lunch*, they can list pairs of words in the material that match the body part of the animal with the action. For example: nose/smells and pointed beak/pecks. Encourage students to find pictures of other animals in magazines and write action words that describe what the animals' parts do.

What's the Result? What do all of the parts have in common? They help the animal survive.

Multi-Age Classroom Divide the students into appropriate groups and have each group choose a particular part of the world. Invite the students to do the activity by finding animals from different parts of the world.

---

2. Guide the Discussion

Choose from the following strategies to facilitate discussion.

 Meeting Individual Needs

Students Acquiring English Have students demonstrate their understanding by role-playing the adaptive behaviors they read about in this resource. Ask them to describe the specialized body parts and to teach their classmates the equivalent words in their native languages.

Connecting to the Activities

- *The Right Beak for the Job, pp. E38–E39*
- **Why are the beaks of the parrots and cockatoos in the tropical rain forests different from the kinds of beaks you explored?** In rain forests, fruits, nuts, and insects are more common food sources than pond wildlife. Parrots and cockatoos need strong beaks to eat seeds, nuts, and fruit.
- **You saw how birds' beaks are adapted for getting the food in their particular habitats, or homes. How do birds use other body parts and behaviors to help them find their food?** Flying birds use their wings to explore their environment for food and their eyes to locate food. Birds that live on both water and land use their feet to paddle around in the search for food; they may have webbed feet. Some birds, such as hawks and eagles, have sharp claws and use their talons to grab food.

 Using Math *Students should indicate that they would use 2 cups of sugar with 8 cups of water.*

Making Inferences

- **What other adaptations can you think of by which plants ensure their survival?** Possible answers include the colorful flowers and pleasant fragrances with which plants attract the birds and insects needed to aid pollination, and some pine cones that require intense heat to sprout that grow only after a forest fire to take advantage of newly open spaces in the sun.

Making Comparisons

- **Chimpanzees and sea otters use tools to locate and gather food. How does this compare with the use of tools by people?** It is actually very similar, although people prepare tools in advance for a variety of tasks while the animals described in the resource fashion tools on the spot or use whatever rocks or other natural materials happen to be available. The chimpanzee learns to peel bark from a stick to catch termites. People often use natural materials to make the tools and weapons they need.

The flamingo uses its bill as a strainer to trap tiny plants, shrimp, and snails found in shallow muddy waters. In the tropical rain forest, parrots and cockatoos use their strong beaks to crack nuts and seeds or to tear open fruit.

Mealtime Manners

You've seen how some body parts are adaptations for getting food. The behavior of an animal can also be an adaptation for getting food. **Behavior** is the way an animal typically acts in certain situations.

Electric eels, a kind of fish, have a really shocking way of getting food. They catch fish by stunning them with an electric shock! An archerfish catches an insect on a nearby water plant by using its long, tubelike mouthparts to shoot out water drops

An archerfish shoots water at an insect. ▼

that knock the insect into the water. Grasshoppers are able to hop more than a meter (about 3 ft) to search for a meal. That's 20 times the length of a grasshopper's body. If you had the muscle power of a grasshopper, you could jump about 24 m (80 ft)!

Some animals use tools from the environment to gather or eat food. While swimming on its back, the sea otter holds a rock on its belly and uses the rock to break open shells. Chimpanzees eat termites from a stick much the way you eat with a fork.

E42

Science & Math

MEASURING

What to Do Grasshoppers and other tiny insects can jump very far compared to their size. Students in groups can take turns jumping and measuring one another's jumps. Encourage students to list all their jumps in order from the shortest to the longest. Students can find the length or lengths in the middle of the list—the median length. Encourage students to compare the median jump distance with the median student height.

What's the Result? How many body lengths were you able to jump? Students should be able to jump close to one body length. **How does that compare with how many body lengths a 5-cm grasshopper can jump?** A grasshopper can jump many times its body length.

▲ A Venus' flytrap catches an insect for lunch.

◀ A chimpanzee uses a stick to dig for termites and then eats the insects as they crawl along the stick.

They peel the bark from a stick and poke it into a termite mound. When they pull out the stick, it is covered with tasty termite treats!

Other animals stalk, or secretly follow, their food. Have you ever watched a neighborhood cat sneak up on a bird? This method is the same one a leopard uses when it stalks a young gazelle on the African plain.

Plants That Trap Insects

Plants need certain nutrients (nōō′trē ənts). **Nutrients** are substances that provide materials needed for growth. Most plants absorb these nutrients from soil.

Plants have different adaptations to get these nutrients. The Venus' flytrap, sundew, and pitcher plants are known for "eating" insects. By trapping and digesting insects, these plants get nutrients that are missing from the soil in which they grow.

All living things need nutrients that food provides. You can see that plants and animals have many adaptations that help them get food. ■

E43

Science & Social Studies

RESEARCHING

What to Do For thousands of years, people have trained certain animals as working partners. The Asian elephant has been trained to transport goods, perform in circuses, and pull down trees. Other animals, such as guide dogs, assist people with special needs. Students will enjoy reading about other animals that have been trained to help humans, such as horses. Encourage students to research working animals and prepare a bulletin-board display on the topic.

What's the Result? What adaptations do these animals have that make them useful to people? Students may suggest strength, speed, endurance, keen senses of sight or hearing, intelligence, and loyalty.

Making Comparisons

• **The resource describes animals and plants that trap their food. How are they different?** The animals use a variety of behavioral adaptations to follow and catch their food; unable to move about, the plants use modified plant parts to trap insects. **How are they alike?** They are the same in that they both use methods to obtain needed nutrients.

3. Assess Understanding

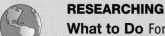 Working in pairs, students can create an imaginary animal and an imaginary habitat, or environment, for it. The environment should include the kind of food the animal eats. Students can draw pictures and write paragraphs to show and explain how the animal's body parts and behaviors are adapted for catching its food. Challenge other groups to try to figure out what the animal eats based on its description.

Reading Focus Answer

Animals have adaptations, such as special body parts, that help them get food. Examples include extraordinary vision, hearing, sense of smell, sharp claws, beaks, and fangs. Animals also have behaviors to help them get food such as stalking their prey, using tools, and hopping. Plants use roots to take in water and nutrients and some plants catch insects.

Science Processor You may wish to have students use the CD-ROM Writer and Painter to write and illustrate their paragraphs.

A Quick Tongue

Reading Focus Focus on the *graphic*, asking students what four body parts they will read about in the notes. Explain they will need to read the paragraph on page E45 to give a complete answer to the question.

1. Get Ready

Vocabulary
Science Term camouflage
Support Term chameleon

Discussion Starter
• **How does the chameleon use its body parts to get food?** It locates prey with its eyes, and it catches prey with its tongue.

2. Guide the Discussion

Connecting to the Activities
• *The Right Beak for the Job, p. E38*
• **How might lizards that live in different habitats differ from chameleons?** They might have different feet if they don't live in trees, eat a different type of food, or use other methods of camouflage.

 Meeting Individual Needs

Early Finishers Students can cut lizard shapes out of newspaper classified ads, white paper, and black paper. Then they can discover the value of changing colors as they "walk" the three lizards across the three kinds of paper.

3. Assess Understanding

 Students can work in pairs to draw a chameleon, label each part that helps it find and catch food, and write a sentence about how each part is adapted to do the job it does.

Reading Focus Answer

A chameleon is adapted to its environment with adaptations for protection, such as eyes that move separately, a strong tail to curl around branches, and the ability to change colors. It has a sticky, long, quick tongue for catching food.

A Quick Tongue

Reading Focus How is a chameleon adapted to its environment?

In the trees of a tropical forest, a chameleon walks along the branches in search of prey. The chameleon seems to be moving in slow motion. How can such a slow animal ever catch a fast-moving insect? The chameleon has some unusual adaptations for getting its food. Find out about them on these pages.

ODD EYES The chameleon's eyes look odd because each eye can move separately. With this adaptation, the chameleon can keep one eye on its prey while the other eye looks for predators.

WHAT A TAIL! A chameleon moves high up in the trees. If it loses its balance, it can curl its strong tail around a branch to keep from falling.

NEAT FEET The chameleon's foot has three toes joined on one side and two toes joined on the other side. The V-shaped foot is good for grabbing onto branches.

E44

INVESTIGATE FURTHER!

RESEARCH

Students can work in pairs of small groups to research their animal. Suggest that students develop a schedule for observing their animal at different times of the day. They may wish to take photos of the animal that illustrate various adaptations such as getting food, protecting itself from cold, finding a mate, moving, and so on. The photos can be glued to the posters for display.

A TALENTED TONGUE The chameleon's tongue is very long—sometimes as long as its entire body. At the end of its tongue is a sticky patch that prey can get stuck on. When inside the chameleon's mouth, the tongue is folded much like an accordion. When prey comes within range, the chameleon shoots out its tongue. Its tongue moves so fast that it would be hard for you to see it move.

Difficult to Spot

The chameleon has a good chance of surprising its prey. That's because of **camouflage** (kam'ə-fläzh)—the ability to blend in with the surroundings. Besides helping the chameleon sneak up on its prey, camouflage makes it hard for predators to spot the chameleon. ■

INVESTIGATE FURTHER!

RESEARCH

Plants and animals have adaptations that help them survive. With a group, choose an animal from your community. What kinds of adaptations does it have? Create a poster of your animal describing its adaptations and show the poster to your classmates.

INVESTIGATION 1 WRAP-UP

REVIEW

1. Describe how body parts help living things get food.

2. Describe how behaviors help living things get food.

CRITICAL THINKING

3. Are humans the only living things that use tools? Argue for or against this theory based on the behaviors of sea otters and chimpanzees.

4. Invent an animal. Draw your animal, showing the kinds of adaptations it would have for getting food. Explain your animal's behavior for getting food.

E45

Close the Investigation

INVESTIGATION WRAP-UP

REVIEW

1. Body parts such as beaks, tongues, eyes or claws can help animals acquire food from places that would otherwise be difficult to reach or see.

2. Behaviors such as the way an electric eel stuns its prey, or the way a chimpanzee captures termites using a stick, enable animals to catch food more easily.

CRITICAL THINKING

3. Students should consider the differences and similarities between tool use in humans versus animals. *(Evaluating, Analyzing)*

4. Students may create a variety of animals and adaptations, and they should reflect an understanding of the concept. *(Generating Ideas, Expressing Ideas)*

CHALLENGE

Students can review the food chains and food webs they read about and illustrated in Chapter 1 of this unit. Have pairs of students write about and demonstrate how each animal in the chain or web has adaptations for getting and eating its food.

FOLLOWING UP

Baseline Assessment Return to the class list of animals and how they get food. For each animal on the list, ask students to discuss how its body parts and behaviors are adapted for getting and eating food.

Reteaching Discuss the investigation subconcept with students. Together, make a chart entitled *Adaptations for Getting Food* that summarizes the data about the animals. Use these headings: *Animal, Food, Body Part*, and *Behavior*. Help students complete the chart using words and phrases and/or simple drawings.

Use *Science Notebook*, TRB p. 52.

Assessment

Portfolio

Write a Story Encourage students to write a brief story about an animal or plant, describing how it uses two of its adaptations for getting food. The adaptations may be physical or behavioral.

Investigation Review ▶
Use *Investigation Review* p. 113 in the *Teacher Resource Book*.

Investigation Review

Name _____ Date _____

Draw a line from the adaptation on the left to the phrase on the right that best describes how it helps the animal.

1. chameleon's eyes — catch and eat large fish
2. hummingbird's long beak and tongue — watch for predator and prey at same time
3. bear's claws and teeth — paralyze and kill prey
4. snake's poison fangs — sip nectar from flower

Use the clues below to unscramble the letters of each word.

5. I am a parrot. I use my strong ____ to crack nuts.

   K B E A ____ **BEAK**

6. I am a sea otter. I get some of my food by using a rock as a ____.

   O L O T ____ **TOOL**

7. I am a leopard. I can catch a gazelle by behaving in a certain way. I ____, or secretly follow and sneak up on, my prey.

   T L K S A ____ **STALK**

8. Animals in nature must work hard to get food. Their task is made easier by their ____.

   P T T O N A D S A I A ____ **ADAPTATIONS**

Process Skills
Hypothesizing

Lower light levels at night make it more difficult to see. While night hunters usually have vision that is adapted to the dark, a sharp sense of hearing helps them locate prey before they can see it. Hypothesize why owls, bats, and other night hunters have highly developed senses of hearing. Write your hypothesis on a separate sheet of paper.

Start
the Investigation

HOW ARE LIVING THINGS ADAPTED FOR PROTECTION?
pages E46–E57

Planner

Subconcept Living things vary in their adaptations for protection, including repellent body parts or chemicals, mimicking dangerous creatures, defensive behaviors, and camouflage.

Objectives
- **Identify** defensive adaptations of organisms.
- **Describe** how chemical adaptations of many plants can be used by people as medicines.

Pacing 3–4 class periods

Science Terms parasites

Activate Prior Knowledge

Baseline Assessment Ask: **How do you think animals and plants protect themselves from their enemies?** Save a class list for Following Up.

HOW ARE LIVING THINGS ADAPTED FOR PROTECTION?

Danger! What do you do? Do you run or hide? Do you stand as still as you can? Living things have different adaptations to protect themselves. Find out about these adaptations in Investigation 2.

Activity

Blending In

Frogs, spiders, and birds are just a few of the predators that eat insects. How do insects protect themselves? This activity will help you find out.

MATERIALS
- colored paper
- colored markers, colored pencils, or crayons
- scissors
- tape
- *Science Notebook*

Procedure

1. Your job is to **design** and **draw** a new kind of insect—one that could hide from predators in your classroom. Look around your classroom for different colors, shapes, and patterns that your insect could blend with and not be easily seen.

2. To draw your insect, use any or all of the drawing materials listed. Remember, your insect must have camouflage so that it blends in and is hard to find.

E46

Activity Blending In

Preview *Students focus on camouflage as an animal defense and should find that the insects that most closely resemble the background are the hardest to find.*

1. Get Ready

 INDIVIDUAL　　　　　🕐 **45 MINUTES**

Key Science Process Skills make and use models, predict, describe, hypothesize, infer

Safety Review safety precautions with students. Caution students to be careful with scissors.

👤 Meeting Individual Needs

STUDENTS ACQUIRING ENGLISH

To demonstrate to students the importance of camouflage in their designs, find pictures of living things that illustrate camouflage as a defense. You might find pictures of different types of bears, including a polar bear and a black bear, and place them both on a snowy, winter background and then on a picture of a dark cave. Challenge students to try to find them. Discuss how such coloration might help the polar bear survive. You could extend the activity by asking students how they might camouflage themselves to be less visible in certain places inside or outside of the classroom.

VISUAL/SPATIAL

Step 3

3. When you have finished drawing your insect, cut it out. Your teacher will tell you when to "hide" your insect. **Predict** where your insect will be hardest to find. Then put your insect in that place. If your insect hides on the wall, use a very small piece of tape to attach it. See if others can find it.

4. In your *Science Notebook,* **describe** what your insect looks like in its hiding place.

Analyze and Conclude

1. Which insect in your class was the hardest to find? **Hypothesize** why it was hard to find that insect.

2. **Infer** how the color, shape, or size of your insect helped it hide. **Explain** your answer.

3. **Predict** what would happen to an insect that didn't have any way to hide from predators. How might such an insect be able to survive?

E47

UNIT PROJECT LINK

Research how animals of the tropical rain forest are adapted to their environment. Construct some rain forest animals and attach them to your mural. Make some camouflaged animals and "hide" them among the plants. Also attach predators and their prey to show a food web.

TechnologyLink
For more help with your Unit Project, go to **www.eduplace.com**.

UNIT PROJECT LINK

Encourage students to find out about all kinds of animals. Mammals, insects, amphibians, reptiles, birds, and fish all live in tropical rain forests. Ask the students to record notes on *Science Notebook,* TRB p. 55. Then use Unit Project Masters 3 and 4 (TRB pp. 18–19) to research information on rain-forest animals.

**Technology**Link
Have students visit **www.eduplace.com** to link with on-line experts who can provide help with the Unit Project.

---

2. Guide the Procedure

- For best results, you may wish to display colorful book covers around the room and place colorful pictures on the walls and bulletin boards to provide places for students to hide their insects.

- Students can line up in the hall with their insects and go into the classroom one by one to hide them.

- Suggest that students record the amount of time it takes to find each camouflaged insect.

Have students draw their insects and answer questions on *Science Notebook,* TRB, pp. 53–54.

Science Processor You may wish to have students use the CD-ROM Spreadsheet to record the length of time it took to find each camouflaged insect.

3. Assess Performance

Process Skills Checklist
- Did students follow directions when **making the model** insect? Were they able to design an insect that blended in with its environment?

- Were students' **predictions** reasonable regarding where their insects would be hardest to find?

- Were students able to **hypothesize** why a particular insect was hardest to find?

Analyze and Conclude
1. Students should hypothesize that the insect that took the longest time to find was the hardest to find. Most probably it blended in well with its surroundings.

2. The more an insect's characteristics matched the background, the better hidden it was. An insect that matched the color, pattern, and shape of its background would be nearly invisible.

3. Students should predict that an insect with no way to hide from predators would have to escape by moving faster than its enemies, or would need another defense, such as a stinger. If it couldn't escape, then these insects would die out.

Hiding Out and Other Defenses

Reading Focus Give students a headstart at answering the Reading Focus question by asking them to *preview* the resource. Have them read each section heading and the first one or two sentences.

1. Get Ready

Vocabulary
Science Term parasite
Support Terms defense, survival

Background
- There is a wide variety of animal and plant defenses in nature. In addition to the mechanisms presented in Hiding Out and Other Defenses, some animals' homes provide protection against predators as well as harsh climatic or weather conditions. For example, rabbits have holes into which they can flee; cactus wrens in Africa's Namib Desert build their nests in spiky cactus plants. Other defenses include body parts such as the deer's antlers, special skills such as the hare's great running speed, and highly developed senses such as the sense of smell of an elephant's trunk. Some animals warn others of their kind of approaching danger. Penguins in the Antarctic flap their wings and call to warn other penguins of the presence of leopard seals.

- The main plant defenses are aimed at the animals that feed upon them. These animals range from tiny insects that suck sap or chew leaves to large mammals, such as elephants, that eat entire plants. Many plants have a covering of fine hairs on the surface of their leaves, which keeps off small insects. In addition to those described in the resource, plant defenses include keeping away the larger animals by "stinging." For example, the chemicals released by the nettle's sting cause painful irritations. The teasel plant has an unusual defense. Pairs of its leaves form cups that fill with water during a rain. Insects that try to eat the leaves drown in the water.

Hiding Out and Other Defenses

Reading Focus What are some adaptations that help plants and animals protect themselves?

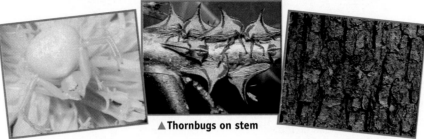

▲ Crab spider on flower

▲ Thornbugs on stem

▲ Tulip tree beauty moth on tree bark

You Can't See Me
Hide-and-seek is fun. But animals in nature must stay safe from enemies and catch food to eat. How they play the game can be a matter of life or death! The activity on pages E46 and E47 shows how camouflage is an important adaptation for defense for many animals. When a young spotted fawn is left alone, it can keep very still and blend in with the forest floor. This keeps predators from seeing the fawn.

An insect called a katydid has wings that look like the leaves of the trees it lives on. Its wings even have brown spots that look like spots found on real leaves. In the photos above, how does camouflage help the animals hide?

E48

Science & Literature

AESOP'S FABLES

What to Do In "The Fox and the Cat," one of Aesop's fables, a fox brags to a cat that he has lots of tricks for escaping from packs of dogs. The cat admits that she has only one way—to run up a tree. When a pack of dogs comes at them, the fox cannot decide which of his tricks to use, while the cat quickly scrambles to safety up a tree. Discuss the difference between describing realistic animal behavior and imaginary behavior in which the writer pretends that animals have human characteristics. See *Aesop & Company, With Scenes From His Legendary Life* by Barbara Bader (Houghton Mifflin Company, 1991).

What's the Result? Encourage students to stage a performance of the fable for another class.

The thorns on a rose are a sharp defense. ▼

Don't Come Too Close!

Some plants have sharp thorns or bristles that help protect them from being eaten. An animal that has nibbled on a sweet-smelling rose and gotten pricked by a thorn, for example, is not likely to make that mistake again.

Some plants contain poisonous or irritating chemicals that keep many animals away. Have you ever touched poison ivy or poison sumac? If so, you know that days of skin sores and itching can result. Because of these effects, many people have learned to stay away from these plants.

Sometimes a plant's defense is its bitter taste. For this reason, some people plant marigold plants around their vegetable gardens. Rabbits are often attracted to the bright orange and yellow colors of these flowers.

◄ A katydid stays safe because predators mistake it for a leaf.

A marigold's bitter taste keeps it safe from hungry animals. ▶

E49

Integrating the Sciences

EARTH SCIENCE

What to Do **How are organisms camouflaged that live where there are few plants?** They must blend in with the rocks and soil. Many desert lizards and insects are rough and mottled with rock-like colors. Manta rays lie on the ocean bottom, blending perfectly with the sandy background. Because the colors of rocks and soil vary from place to place, the colors of organisms that live there vary. Students can use their knowledge of local rocks and soils to hypothesize what colors and shapes of organisms would blend in best.

What's the Result? Have students explore a local area free of plants to see what colors of organisms live there.

Discussion Starter

- **How do your pets protect themselves from other animals or from dangers?** Students might respond that dogs and cats may use body parts such as teeth and claws or, if they are frightened, they may hide or run away; rabbits have protective coloring that helps them hide; and some reptiles and snakes have poisonous bites.

- **What kinds of predators do plants have?** Students' responses might include small animals such as insects and larger animals such as people, rabbits, or deer.

- **Have you had any experiences with defenses plants use as protection?** Students might describe experiences with poison ivy and poison oak or with plants such as cactuses that have sharp parts.

2. Guide the Discussion

Choose from the following strategies to facilitate discussion.

 Meeting Individual Needs

Students Acquiring English Encourage students to discuss with classmates any animals or plants from their native countries that have interesting ways of defending themselves. Remind students that hiding or camouflage can be as important or useful as having thorns or fangs. If they are familiar with these animals, have students teach classmates the names of the animals in the Resource in their native languages.

Analyzing Data

- **For what purpose do katydids use their camouflage?** Katydids' green coloration closely resembles the leaves in which they hide. This allows them to capture and eat other insects.

- **How is the coloring of fawns' fur used differently from the camouflage of the katydids?** Fawns use their coloring to blend into the forest and hide from their predators; the katydids use their coloration to surprise their prey and obtain food.

Connecting to the Activities

- *Blending In, p. E46*
- **How did the insect you designed defend itself?** Students may suggest that they used size and shape as well as color to camouflage their insects to protect them from predators.

Making Inferences

- **What defense does a wasp have?** It can sting.

- **Japanese beetles were introduced into the United States from Japan in 1917. They can fly and eat rose petals. Why do you think the thorns and spiky leaves do not protect the plant?**

Meeting Individual Needs

Gifted and Talented Students may be interested to learn about the variety of ways animals communicate with each other. Have them research the topic and present a report to the class. Encourage them to illustrate their reports. Some useful references are: *Communication* by David Burnie (Franklin Watts, 1992), *Bees Dance and Whales Sing: The Mysteries of Animal Communication* by Margery Facklam (Sierra Club Books, 1992), and *Animal Communication* by Janet McDonnell (Child's World, Inc. 1989).

Students Acquiring English Collect a variety of animal coverings. A local pet store may be able to provide snakeskin, shells, dog hairs, and feathers. A fish market may give you fish scales. Let students examine each kind of covering. Discuss the ways each skin protects the animal.

> **Math Hint** *Help students recognize that the porcupine in the picture obviously has many more than 30 quills, and not all of the quills are visible. Therefore, it is more likely to have 30,000 quills.*

But after tasting the marigolds, the rabbits usually go elsewhere in search of more pleasant-tasting plants to nibble.

Animals that are covered with quills or spines have a defense against being eaten. No animal wants to eat quills or spines. The quills of porcupines and spines of hedgehogs provide prickly protection.

Most of the time a puffer fish does not look prickly. But when it is attacked, or when it fears attack, it can suck in water and blow itself up into a spine-covered ball. Its shape, size, and spines make it impossible for even a large fish to eat the puffer fish!

You're Copying Me!

Some animals are protected from enemies because they look like other, more dangerous, animals. Most wasps and hornets have black and yellow stripes. Animals that have been stung by these dangerous insects learn to avoid them. Some harmless beetles also have black and yellow stripes. These beetles may not be attacked by predators because they look like the more dangerous hornets and wasps.

 Do you think a porcupine is more likely to have 30 quills or 30,000 quills? Explain your answer.

A relaxed puffer fish ▼   **An alarmed puffer fish under attack ▼**

 E50

Science & the Arts

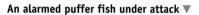

PAINTING

What to Do Using a variety of art materials, invite the students to make paintings of the more colorful animals discussed in *Hiding Out and Other Defenses*. Encourage them to include some of the animals' habitats. One reference for photos of other animals include *Hiding Out: Camouflage in the Wild* by James Martin (Crown Publishers, Inc., 1993).

What's the Result? Students can investigate where the animals they painted live and include that information in their paintings.

Science Processor The wide variety of Animal Data Packs included on the CD-ROM can be used to research this activity. The Painter could also be used for drawing the animals.

Other copycats include the harmless kingsnake, which looks like the poisonous coral snake. Both snakes have red, yellow, and black stripes, but the colors are arranged differently. Although the creature on the right looks like a snake, it's actually a caterpillar from a Costa Rican rain forest. Some butterflies and moths fool predators because of two bright spots on their wings. The spots look like the eyes of large owls.

Tricked You, Didn't I?

The opossum is famous for tricking predators into thinking it's dead. The trick works because the opossum's enemies eat only freshly killed meat. The squid also tricks its enemy. It sprays an inklike substance in its enemy's face. This inky cloud prevents the enemy from seeing the squid. While the enemy is blinded, the squid swims away.

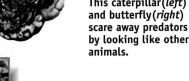

This caterpillar (*left*) and butterfly (*right*) scare away predators by looking like other animals.

The kingsnake (*right*) is a copycat of the poisonous coral snake (*left*).

E51

Science, Technology & Society

INFECTIONS

What to Do People are almost always at risk of being invaded by tiny organisms. Infections carried by these organisms can cause sickness or even death. Antibiotics are substances that are used to protect humans, farm animals, and pets from infections by bacteria. Encourage students to investigate other ways they can reduce their chances of getting an infection. Have them make a list of their findings.

What's the Result? How many things do you do by habit to protect yourself against infection? Actions might include washing hands before eating, brushing and flossing teeth, cleaning a cut with soap and water, and storing perishable food in the refrigerator.

WITHDRAWN
FIRELANDS COLLEGE
BGSU FIRELANDS LIBRARY
LIBRARY

Making Comparisons

- **What is the same about the defense mechanisms of turtles, hermit crabs, and pill bugs? How are they different?** All three animals use some kind of hard covering to protect themselves against predators. The animals in the first group carry it around as a body covering; the second group finds coverings in the shells of other animals; the pill bugs curl up so that only the hard body coverings are exposed.

- **How do the black-and-yellow striped wasps and hornets use color in the same way the coral snake does?** They all use color to advertise that they sting. The color warns their predators.

Thinking About the Data

- **Why do you think the copycat organisms such as the harmless beetles and the butterflies with spots on their wings were successful in defending themselves?** Animals who had encounters with the animals they closely resembled would avoid them as well. As a result, more of them survived than those without those colors.

- **How does this defense mechanism differ from the camouflage that you studied earlier?** Students should conclude that these animals survive by standing out (looking like more dangerous animals) rather than by blending in with their surroundings.

Drawing Conclusions

- **How does the defense of the pufferfish work?** When the pufferfish inflates, its body enlarges and nearly invisible spines appear, making it too big and prickly for larger fish to attack it.

- **What body parts do you think have been modified in the pufferfish and the porcupine to produce their spines?** Students should infer that the pufferfish's spines are modified scales, and the porcupine's quills are modified hairs that have actually fused or grown together.

Making Inferences

- The ostrich's defense of its chicks would seem to place it in danger. **How do you think such defenses enable the ostrich to survive?** Students should infer that the adult bird is better able to outrun predators and return to its chicks by using this method of distracting its enemies. Such behavior patterns also enable more chicks to survive a period when they are very vulnerable.

Making Comparisons

- **How are the defenses used by the ostrich, the lizard, and the opossum similar?** Each animal places itself in a dangerous position and uses some strategy to distract its predators. **How are they different?** The opossum's trick works because its enemies will not eat a dead animal. The ostrich's method is to fool predators into thinking it is injured so that they will chase it rather than its young. The lizard literally loses a part of its body to make its escape.

 Science in Literature

Piranhas and Other Wonders of the Jungle
by Q. L. Pearce

Students can work in pairs or small groups to design a "Believe It or Not" poster that includes amazing, but true, information from the book. Encourage students to include pictures on their posters.

▲ **An ostrich protecting its young**

Some lizards have a last-chance defense against predators by losing their tails! The tail continues to twitch after it has dropped off the lizard. This tricks the predator, which pounces on the tail and eats it while the rest of the lizard escapes!

Many birds pretend to be hurt to protect their chicks. The African ostrich flaps its wings and cries out when a predator heads toward its young. This gets the attention of the predator, which goes after the adult bird instead of the chicks.

Going My Way?

Some animal behaviors are adaptations for protection against parasites (par'ə sītz). **Parasites** are creatures that live on or in other living things and harm them. Adaptations that protect against parasites have led to some very unusual friendships.

 Science in Literature

Piranhas and Other Wonders of the Jungle
by Q. L. Pearce
Illustrated by Mary Ann Fraser
Julian Messner, 1990

E52

RIVER SHARK EATS COW!

"If you saw a list of the world's most dangerous fish, you would likely find the piranha near the top. . . . This fish is equipped with an arsenal of stabbing, cutting teeth. . . . An animal as large as a cow can be devoured in just a few minutes, leaving nothing but bare bones."

Discover more interesting facts about rain forest life in the book *Piranhas and Other Wonders of the Jungle* by Q. L. Pearce. Learn how different jungle creatures survive and protect themselves by adapting to their environment.

Integrating the Sciences

EARTH SCIENCE

What to Do Discuss how animals that live in areas with extreme climates—very hot or very cold—have adaptations to protect them from these conditions. Polar bears have thick fur to protect them from the cold. Snakes and other desert animals burrow under the sand to avoid the heat. Encourage students to make a poster showing how animals in their area of the country are adapted to the climate.

What's the Result? **What climatic conditions do animals in our area face? Give some examples of how they protect themselves?** Specific answers will depend on the region, but might include responding to changes in temperature, adapting to flood conditions, and surviving forest fires.

Birds called oxpeckers eat a meal off the hide of a rhinoceros. ▶

Oxpeckers, or tickbirds, are small African songbirds. These birds eat ticks and other annoying parasites off the tough skin of the rhinoceros, buffalo, and elephant. By allowing the birds to remain on them, these large animals protect themselves from parasites. In exchange, the birds are protected from predators as they dine. Few animals would attack a bird sitting on a fierce rhino.

Another unusual friendship occurs in coral reefs under the sea. A small fish called the cleaner fish removes parasites from the skin, gills, and mouth of many other reef fish. The coral reef fish are protected from parasites, and the cleaner fish has an easily found meal.

As you can see, plants and animals have many defenses. All are a matter of survival. ■

◀ The arrows point to two cleaner fish eating parasites from a coral reef fish.

E53

Making Comparisons

- **Which animal do you think benefits more—the rhinoceros or the oxpecker? Why do you think so?** Students' opinions may vary, but guide them to understand that in most relationships of this type, both partners benefit equally.

Making Inferences

- **Why do you think the "hitchhikers" described —the tickbirds and oxpeckers—are not harmful to the animals they ride on?** Students should infer that the skins of the rhino, buffalo, and elephant are too tough for the birds' beaks to hurt them. In each case, the body covering of the "host" is not food for the hitchhiker. Some may suggest that if the "hitchhikers" did hurt their hosts, the hosts wouldn't tolerate them.

3. Assess Understanding

Students can work in groups of five or six to play the game "What am I?" Students take turns describing the defense of an animal discussed in the resource; for example, "I defend myself with a bitter taste. What am I?" Other students name the animal.

Reading Focus Answer

Adaptations that plants and animals have for protection include camouflage, thorns, poisons, bitter taste, spines, looking like a dangerous animal (mimicry), playing dead, tricking the enemy, pretending to be hurt or dead, and relationships with other animals which allow them to be rid of parasites.

Science & Writing

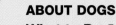

ABOUT DOGS

What to Do Explain to students that long ago when people lived in small hunting groups, one of the first animals that humans adopted as a helper was the dog. Some people believe humans adopted and tamed the dog because together they became more successful hunters. Other people believe the dog adopted people because it could scavenge from their food remains and sit by a warm fire. Encourage students to write a story about the first domestic dog, illustrating the hypothesis they think makes the most sense.

What's the Result? Invite students to share their stories with the class. **What other benefits do people now get from having a pet dog?** Students may mention companionship and security.

Medicines from Nature

Reading Focus Point out to students that as they read the resource they will have to *draw conclusions* to answer the Reading Focus question.

1. Get Ready

Vocabulary

Support Terms pioneers, chemicals, maize

Background

- Plants were the main source of medicines in ancient times. People used the trial-and-error method to discover which plants to use for specific diseases. For example, the ancient Egyptians used the oil from the beans of the castor oil plant as a general remedy. The Chinese have used the ginseng root to aid recovery from illness for about 5,000 years.

- Today, at least 40 percent of the prescriptions filled in the United States contain drugs with primary active ingredients that come from natural sources—about 25 percent from plants, 3 percent from animals, and 13 percent from microorganisms. Eventually, as many as 5,000 of the world's approximately 500,000 plant species might be sources of valuable drugs.

Discussion Starter

- **What are some different ways people use plants?** Students might respond that plants are used for food, to provide beauty and fragrance inside and outside, to provide shelter from the sun and rain, and to build and heat homes.

- **We will be reading about medicine from plants. What is a medicine? What do you think people mean by the words *preventive medicine?*** Students may respond that medicine is something you take when you are sick or hurt to make you better. When talking about preventive medicine, encourage discussion of healthy habits—proper nutrition, exercise, and adequate rest.

Medicines From Nature

Reading Focus How is nature like a drugstore?

When you're sick, a family member probably gets you medicine from the drugstore. In some places, though, you might just be told, "Take a hike!"

Hitting the Nature Trail

People all over the world hike along woodland paths to find healing plants. They rely on nature's drugstore for relief. If you live in the Ozark Mountains of Missouri, your family might brew spicebush tea to bring down your fever. If you live in the Appalachian Mountains and have a stomachache, someone might serve you a gentle drink of slippery elm bark tea. This treatment was used by pioneers over 200 years ago.

Plants produce chemicals that help in their protection and survival. The chemicals are in leaves, bark, roots, blossoms, and seeds. The use of these chemicals as medicine goes back thousands of years.

Medicines From Living Things

Many plant parts and chemicals, as well as animal parts, have been used as medicines. The ancient Greeks used a powder made from substances in the bark of the willow tree to treat pain and reduce fever.

The main ingredient in aspirin is similar to a substance in the bark of the willow tree. ▶

ASPIRIN

E54

Science Around the World

MEDICINE STUDY

What to Do The Native Americans of North and South America used a wide variety of natural products for medicine. Students can find out about the medicines used by the Aztecs and the Incas in particular. Have groups prepare reports to share with the class. Helpful references include *The Aztecs* by Frances F. Berdan (California State University, 1989) and *The Incas* by Sarita Kensall (Macmillan Publishing Company, 1992).

What's the Result? How could the sharing of medicinal knowledge among cultures be helpful? Sharing knowledge of plants that cure illnesses helps everyone.

In the 1890s a German chemist studied the substances in willow bark. In a laboratory, he developed a similar substance, aspirin. Today aspirin is probably the most-widely-used medicine in the world.

Early settlers in America often relied on medicines used by Native Americans. The Cherokees used the bark of the sassafras tree to treat sores. They then applied a soothing paste of powdered maize, or corn, and soft turkey down feathers!

Navajo (nav'ə hō) healers still use the root of the strong-smelling osha plant. Not only does osha root help treat colds, but it also has been found to keep snakes away.

▲ The Ohlone people in California us[e] the roots of the horsetail plant to make a syrup for coughs.

A Cherokee helps heal an early settler with bark and powdered maize. ▶

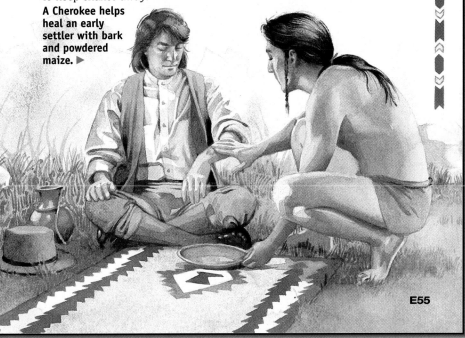

E55

Science & Writing

FIELD GUIDES

What to Do Students may not know that some plants are poisonous to eat. Some examples are the bulbs of the daffodil and the hyacinth, the entire lily-of-the-valley plant, morning glory seeds, and the leaves of many oak and cherry trees. Discuss the importance of not eating anything that you aren't sure is safe to eat. See *Poisonous Plants* by Suzanne M. Coil (Franklin Watts, 1991). Have students make a field guide to poisonous plants in your area.

What's the Result? What advantage might it be to a plant to be poisonous? Students may suggest that poison is a defense for some plants.

2. Guide the Discussion

Choose from the following strategies to facilitate discussion.

Thinking Critically

• **How do you think humans first discovered that certain plants would cure certain diseases or help people recover from certain diseases?** Students may respond that they probably tried out whatever was available in their environment. Encourage discussion about the trial-and-error method of solving problems.

Making Inferences

• **Are all plants safe?** No, many can be poisonous.

• **In the resource, *Hiding Out and Other Defenses* you learned how some plants protect themselves. In this resource, you are learning how people use plants in medicines. Do you think plants might need protection from people? Why?** Students may suggest that humans are animals that consume plants just like many other animals do. Encourage discussion about the need to guard against cutting or removing too many plants of one kind, especially when the temptation is strong, such as when the plant could be used to cure or prevent diseases.

3. Assess Understanding

Have groups of students write an editorial about why plants are important resources for people and why the wide variety of plants throughout the world should be preserved.

Science Processor Encourage students to use the CD-ROM Writer to write their editorials.

Reading Focus Answer

From the earliest recorded history people have used plants for medicines. Today, nearly half of all prescribed drugs contain some chemicals from nature.

Close the Investigation

INVESTIGATION WRAP-UP

REVIEW

1. Students may suggest poisons, bitter taste, or thorns.

2. Students should answer that camouflage helps an animal hide from its predators.

CRITICAL THINKING

3. According to the definition, an adaptation is a behavior or part of a living thing that helps it to survive, so an animal's ability to learn is an adaptation. Student responses should reflect an understanding of this definition. **(Analyzing, Generating Ideas)**

4. Students may describe methods for camouflage or copying other animals. They may also suggest teeth, claws, and methods of escape. **(Generating Ideas, Expressing Ideas)**

CHALLENGE

Have students find out from a local druggist the names of some medicines that contain natural ingredients and what those ingredients are. Make a class chart of the data.

FOLLOWING UP

Baseline Assessment Return to the class list of how the animals and plants illustrated on students' mobiles protect themselves from predators with their parts and behaviors. Ask students to use what they have learned to make any necessary corrections or to add animals or plants to the list.

Reteaching Discuss the investigation subconcept with students. Work with them to make a chart that summarizes the central idea of the defenses of living things.

Use *Science Notebook,* TRB p. 56.

In some places, people use snakes as part of a cure. Some shops in China offer medicines made from snake blood, venom, and skin to improve vision.

Natural First-Aid Kit

Some people keep an aloe plant in the kitchen. Burns from cooking can be soothed by breaking off a fleshy aloe leaf and squeezing its clear liquid onto the burns.

Today nearly half of all prescribed drugs contain at least one chemical from nature. Scientists have climbed mountains and crossed deserts in their search for plants that can be used to produce new medicines.

Scientists are hopeful that many discoveries will be made in tropical rain forests. Most plants in the rain forests haven't yet been identified. The search for medicines from nature continues. ■

Plants and animals of the rain forest may hold new cures. ▶

An aloe plant ▼

INVESTIGATION 2 WRAP-UP

REVIEW

1. Describe two protective adaptations found in plants.

2. How does camouflage protect an animal?

CRITICAL THINKING

3. Is an animal's ability to learn an adaptation? Explain your answer.

4. Imagine you are walking through a forest to observe the animals that live there. Describe some of the adaptations the animals might have to protect themselves.

E56

Assessment

Investigation Review

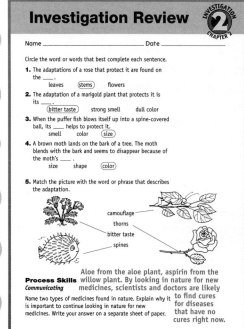

Name _____ Date _____

Circle the word or words that best complete each sentence.

1. The adaptations of a rose that protect it are found on the _____ .
leaves (stems) flowers

2. The adaptation of a marigold plant that protects it is its _____ .
(bitter taste) strong smell dull color

3. When the puffer fish blows itself up into a spine-covered ball, its _____ helps to protect it.
smell color (size)

4. A brown moth lands on the bark of a tree. The moth blends with the bark and seems to disappear because of the moth's _____ .
size shape (color)

5. Match the picture with the word or phrase that describes the adaptation.

camouflage
thorns
bitter taste
spines

Process Skills
Communicating

Name two types of medicines found in nature. Explain why it is important to continue looking in nature for new medicines. Write your answer on a separate sheet of paper.

Aloe from the aloe plant, aspirin from the willow plant. By looking in nature for new medicines, scientists and doctors are likely to find cures for diseases that have no cures right now.

Performance

Debate Have students debate whether an animal depends more upon its body parts or its behavior for protection. Ask students to justify their opinions.

◀ Investigation Review
Use Investigation Review p. 114 in the *Teacher Resource Book.*

REFLECT & EVALUATE

Word Power

Write the letter of the term that best matches the definition. *Not all terms will be used.*

1. The way an animal acts

2. Creatures that live on or in other living things and harm them

3. Behaviors or parts of living things that help them survive

4. Ability to blend in with the surroundings

a. adaptations
b. behavior
c. camouflage
d. nutrients
e. parasites

Check What You Know

Write the term in each pair that best completes each sentence.

1. The shape of a bird's beak is an adaptation for (getting food, protection).

2. By digesting an insect, a Venus' flytrap gets (parasites, nutrients).

3. An opossum pretending to be dead is an example of an adaptive (behavior, body part).

4. An adaptation that helps protect a rose plant is its (leaves, thorns).

5. A cleaner fish eats (predators, parasites) from coral reef fish.

Problem Solving

1. A rabbit begins to eat a plant. But after one bite, the rabbit won't ever eat that plant again. Explain an adaptation the plant might have that protects it from being eaten by the rabbit.

2. Some animals hunt food only at night. The darkness may protect them from predators, but how do they find their food in the dark? Explain how certain senses might be adaptations that help these animals find food in the dark.

 Study the photograph of the lobster. What adaptations does the lobster have for catching food or for protecting itself?

E57

Assessment

Chapter Test

Name _____ Date _____

Problem Solving Each item is worth 10 points.

10. Draw a circle around the adaptations shown. Explain your answers on the lines provided.

Accept any answers that students can justify.

a.
Claws catch and hold fish (food). Eyes locate fish in water.

b.
Rose thorns keep animals from eating the rose plant.

c.
Nose (sense of smell) allows dog to follow a scent trail. Ears allow dog to hear faint noises.

d.
Eagle flies with wings, spots prey with eyes, captures prey with claws (talons).

Chapter Test

Name _____ Date _____

Check What You Know Each item is worth 6 points.

For questions 1–4, circle the letter of the answer that best completes each sentence.

1. One animal that can be camouflaged on the forest floor is a ____.
   a. fawn
   b. yellow jacket
   c. coral snake
   d. blue bird

2. Some animals use tools from the environment to help them gather food. One such animal is the ____.
   a. woodpecker
   b. owl
   c. dog
   d. chimpanzee

3. A(n) ____ is an animal that protects itself by tricking predators into thinking it is dead.
   a. spider
   b. opossum
   c. coral snake
   d. grasshopper

4. Many kinds of medicines are made from ____.
   a. bird feathers
   b. plants
   c. snake blood
   d. insects

Word Power Each item is worth 7 points.

Write the letter of the term that best matches the definition.

5. the ability to blend in with the colors of one's surroundings

6. substance that provides a living thing with the materials needed for growth

7. behavior or part of a living thing that helps it survive in a certain environment

8. a living thing that lives on or in another living thing

9. the way a living thing typically acts in a certain situation

a. adaptation
b. behavior
c. camouflage
d. nutrient
e. parasite

REFLECT & EVALUATE

Word Power

1. b   **2.** e   **3.** a   **4.** c

Check What You Know

1. getting food   **2.** nutrients   **3.** behavior

4. thorns   **5.** parasites

Problem Solving

1. The plant may have a bitter taste or thorns that protect it from being eaten by the rabbit.

2. Animals that hunt at night might have better eyesight, hearing, and/or a better sense of smell than other animals that hunt during daylight.

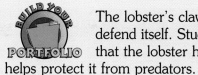 The lobster's claws help it catch food and defend itself. Students may also know that the lobster has a hard shell that helps protect it from predators.

Assess Performance

Student Task

Have students design an animal with adaptations for catching a meal and for protecting itself. Students can draw or use different materials to construct their animal model. Students should offer logical reasons for each adaptation they chose.

Scoring Rubric

Points	What to Look For
3	The student's model clearly shows two types of adaptations—one for catching food and one for protection.
2	The model is generally logical but some aspects are not accurate or described clearly.
1	The model is unclear, illogical, and does not address the concept.

◄ **Chapter Test**

Use pp. 115–116 in the *Teacher Resource Book*.

CHAPTER 3 · LIVING THINGS IN THE ENVIRONMENT

Subconcepts	Activities	Materials
Investigation 1 How Can Living Things Change the Environment? pp. E60–E67		

Living things can alter their environment, and the changes can affect other living things.
 	
Suggested Pacing: 3–4 class periods
 	
National Science Education Standards
    See page E 1c, numbers 3, 6, and 7.
 	
Project 2061 Benchmarks
    See page E 1c, numbers 2 and 4.
	My Neighborhood Keeps Changing!, p. E60
	Science Process Skills: observe; classify; communicate; infer; predict; collect, record, and interpret data
		My Neighborhood Keeps Changing!
		Science Notebook, TRB pp. 61–62

Investigation 2 How Are Living Things Adapted to Their Environments? pp. E68–E76		
Living things have adaptations that enable them to cope with changes in their environment. *Suggested Pacing: 2–3 class periods* **National Science Education Standards** See page E 1c, number 2.	**Keeping Heat In,** p. E68 *Science Process Skills:* measure/use numbers; predict; collect, record, and interpret data; identify and control variables; make hypotheses; experiment; make and use models	**Keeping Heat In** 2 large plastic jars*, 2 small plastic jars*, down feathers*, hot tap water, thermometer*, timer*, *Science Notebook ,* TRB pp. 64–65

Overview
In this chapter students investigate how living things affect their environments and adapt to environmental changes in order to survive.

Chapter Concept
Living things change their environments and respond to changes in their environments.

Theme: Systems
Living things and their environments form ecological systems (ecosystems). Within these systems, living things must adapt to environmental changes to survive.

Advance Preparation	Resources/ Vocabulary	Assessment
My Neighborhood Keeps Changing! None	**Busy Beaver Construction Co.** **People Change the Environment** **Vocabulary:** ecosystem, wetlands **Bringing Back the Buffaloes**	**Chapter 3 Baseline Assessment:** TRB pp. 59–60 **Investigation 1 Baseline Assessment:** TG p. E60 **Investigation 1 Review:** TRB p. 118 **Think It/Write It:** p. E67 TRB p. 63 **Following Up on Baseline Assessment:** TG p. E67 **Portfolio:** TG p. E67
Keeping Heat In None	**Beating the Heat** **When the Going Gets Tough . . .** **Vocabulary:** migrate, hibernation, dormancy	**Investigation 2 Baseline Assessment:** TG p. E68 **Investigation 2 Review:** TRB p. 119 **Think It/Write It:** p. E76 TRB p. 67 **Following Up on Baseline Assessment:** TG p. E76 **Performance:** TG p. E76 **Chapter 3 Summative Assessment:** Reflect and Evaluate: p. E77 Chapter 3 Review/Test: TRB pp. 120–121 *Science Notebook,* TRB pp. 68–69

*Materials in the Equipment Kit   TG= Teaching Guide   TRB= Teacher Resource Book

Chapter Overview

Concept Preview

You may wish to use Transparency E3 to introduce some of the important concepts of the chapter. Students can add to the map as they complete each Activity and Resource. Then they can use the completed map as a study guide. See below for an example of a completed map.

Vocabulary Development

You may use Vocabulary Master E3 at any point in the chapter to provide additional support for the science vocabulary words.

Common Misconceptions

Students might think that the environment and the living things within it remain unchanged.

Introducing the Chapter

Warm-Up Activity

 Tell students that because of some calamity, they have to live outdoors. What would they have to do simply to survive? What further changes would they do to make their life more comfortable? Try to get their answers about what is necessary to survive and then what is necessary to be more comfortable. Food, shelter, and water would be necessary to survive. TVs, computers, chairs, etc. would make their life more comfortable.

Use *Science Notebook*, TRB pp. 59–60.

Discussion Starter

Initiate a discussion about students' current understanding of how environmental changes affect living things.

• **Humans make changes in the environment for their own benefit. Are all these changes good for other animals?** Discuss changes that might be occurring in your community that may not be beneficial to other animals. Such changes might include construction of a mall or the cutting down of trees.

CHAPTER 3

LIVING THINGS IN THE ENVIRONMENT

What living things change the environment the most? If you guessed humans, you're right. And right now people are very quickly changing the country of Brazil. Some of those changes are destroying the environments of plants and animals.

PEOPLE USING SCIENCE

Wildlife Photographer Luiz Claudio Marigo is a Brazilian wildlife photographer. Many of the animals and plants in his photographs no longer exist. His pictures are all that are left of them.

But Luiz Marigo is doing more than recording vanishing animals and their forest homes. He is trying to show his country's wonderful wildlife. Luiz Marigo wants people to save Brazil's forests.

Luiz Marigo's interest in photography began as a child on his first trip to a wildlife area. He knew at once that he would devote himself to capturing nature with his camera.

As you read this chapter, think about the living things that share your environment. How do changes affect the plants, animals, and people around you?

E58

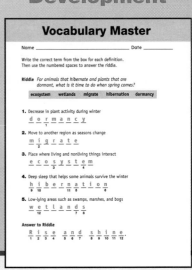

Concept Preview

Transparency

Living things change their environment. These changes often affect other living things.

An action by a living thing	→	creates this change	→	which affects living things in this way.
Example 1	Beavers make a dam.	A pond forms.	A home is created for fish and other animals.
Example 2	People cut down trees in a rain forest.	The forest disappears.	Some animals may become endangered or extinct.
Example 3	People drain water from wetlands.	The land is used for new housing.	Wetland animals must find new homes, or they will die.

▲ **Reading Support Book**
Transparency E3

Vocabulary Development

Vocabulary Master

Name _____ Date _____

Write the correct term from the box for each definition. Then use the numbered spaces to answer the riddle.

Riddle *For animals that hibernate and plants that are dormant, what is it time to do when spring comes?*

| ecosystem | wetlands | migrate | hibernation | dormancy |

1. Decrease in plant activity during winter
d o r m a n c y
1

2. Move to another region as seasons change
m i g r a t e
2

3. Place where living and nonliving things interact
e c o s y s t e m
3   4   5

4. Deep sleep that helps some animals survive the winter
h i b e r n a t i o n
9 10   11 8   6

5. Low-lying areas such as swamps, marshes, and bogs
w e t l a n d s
12   7   8

Answer to Riddle
R i s e   a n d   s h i n e
1 2 3 4   5 6 7   8 9 10 11 12

▲ **Reading Support Book**
Vocabulary Master E3

▲ Luiz Claudio Marigo

◀ A photo by Luiz Marigo of two Brazilian jaguars

E59

Chapter Road Map

 INVESTIGATION 1
HOW CAN LIVING THINGS CHANGE THE ENVIRONMENT?
Activities
My Neighborhood Keeps Changing!✱
Resources
Busy Beaver Construction Co.✱, People Change the Environment✱, Bringing Back the Buffaloes

INVESTIGATION 2
HOW ARE LIVING THINGS ADAPTED TO THEIR ENVIRONMENTS?
Activities
Keeping Heat In✱
Resources
Beating the Heat✱, When the Going Gets Tough...✱

 ## ✱ Pressed for Time?
If you are pressed for time, focus on the Activities and Resources identified by this clock.

 ## Home-School Connection
Distribute the Explore at Home Activity "Fair Weather Friends" (Teacher Resource Book, page 5) to students after they have completed the chapter.

 ## Technology Link
Videotape

Bill Nye the Science Guy *Plants*
At Saguaro National Monument in Arizona, Jeff Kartheiser tours the desert and explains how the cacti and succulents soak up water whenever it is plentiful and store it in fleshy stems and pads for droughts. Bill discusses how cacti defend their precious water against animals that might threaten them. To illustrate how some plants respond to changes in their environment, he explains that certain plants adapt to winter by shutting down food production. (Disney Educational Productions 1-800-295-5010)

Correlation to AIMS

If you use AIMS Activities, you may wish to use the Activity "Table Manners" on pages 111–114 in the *Critters* book to explore how living things adapt to their environment.

Start
the Investigation

How Can Living Things Change the Environment?

pages E60–E67

Planner

Subconcept Living things can alter their environment, and the changes can affect other living things.

Objectives
- **Infer** the causes of change in an environment.
- **Investigate** how changes animals and people make in an environment affect other living things.

Pacing 3–4 class periods

Science Terms ecosystem, wetlands

Activate Prior Knowledge

Baseline Assessment Ask: **What kinds of changes can take place in our environment? Which changes are helpful? Which are harmful?** Have students draw pictures of helpful and harmful changes and save them for use in Following Up.

How Can Living Things Change the Environment?

Have you ever seen a house being built? Big machines are used to move dirt and cut down trees. In Investigation 1, find out how people and other living things change their environments.

Activity

MATERIALS
• Science Notebook

My Neighborhood Keeps Changing!

Think about an old photograph that shows your home or neighborhood. Then think about your home or neighborhood as it is today. What changes have taken place? How do people make changes to their environments?

Dallas, Texas in 1908 ▼

Procedure
1. Observe the two pictures on page E61. The neighborhood shown has changed in many ways over the years. In your *Science Notebook*, **make a list** of all the changes you can find. **Compare** your list with those of other group members to see if there is anything that you missed.

E60

Activity My Neighborhood Keeps Changing!

Preview *Students focus on studying photos and find that people can have an effect on an environment.*

1. Get Ready

 GROUPS OF 4–6   **30 MINUTES**

Key Science Process Skills observe, record, infer, hypothesize

Multi-Age Strategy Students can list their observations about the pictures, then combine their lists with other students' lists.

Meeting Individual Needs

STUDENTS ACQUIRING ENGLISH

Group students who need help learning English with classmates who are fluent in English. Have them work together to list the changes they observe in the pictures of the neighborhood. Encourage them to identify changes in both living and nonliving objects and to record their observations. Then have students discuss who or what caused each change.

VISUAL/SPATIAL

Step 1

2. Look at your list. **Infer** who made the changes. **Talk with your group** and **hypothesize** how the changes affected living things in the area.

Analyze and Conclude

1. What caused the changes in this neighborhood? **Explain** how these changes affected the environment.

2. Think about the neighborhood that you live in. **Predict** what your neighborhood will look like when you grow up. How might people and other living things change your neighborhood?

INVESTIGATE FURTHER!

RESEARCH

Tape-record sounds from your neighborhood. Then bring the tape to school. Have your classmates identify which sounds are made by nature and which are made by people. Hypothesize what your neighborhood may have sounded like 100 years ago.

E61

INVESTIGATE FURTHER!

RESEARCH

Students can work together in small groups of three or four. They should brainstorm ideas about how their neighborhoods might have sounded in the past. Remind them that, 100 years ago, there were no automobiles in the streets or jets in the air. Students can record their sound identifications and hypotheses on *Science Notebook*, TRB, p. 62.

2. Guide the Procedure

- **What kinds of changes would you predict for the neighborhood in the picture during the next ten years?** A garage, handicapped ramp, or another addition might be built onto one of the homes. The trees across the street might be cleared to build a modern development, access to public transportation, or a store. **Who or what might cause these changes?** New owners might move into the house or the current tenants may need other services as they age. Developers might clear the land. Municipal government would be responsible for any new public transportation. **Which changes might help the plants and animals living there?** Planting trees and gardens might provide homes for different small animals or provide new food sources. **Which changes might harm them?** Clearing of the land would eliminate trees and shrubs in which animals live.

 Have students record their lists, inferences, and hypotheses and answer questions on *Science Notebook*, TRB, pp. 61–62.

 Science Processor If you wish, have students use the CD-ROM Painter to draw their own neighborhood, now and/or five years from now.

3. Assess Performance

Process Skills Checklist

- Did students accurately **observe** and **record** the changes in the neighborhood?
- Did students **infer** the sources of the changes? Were their inferences based on their observations?
- Did students **predict** changes in their own neighborhoods? Were their predictions reasonable?

Analyze and Conclude

1. Human activities caused most changes. When the trees were cleared to build the house next door and sidewalks and streets were paved, animals living there had to move. The addition of a garden as well as birdbaths and bird feeders will create new homes and food supplies for some animals.

2. Answers might include people building more houses, stores, parks, or schools; adding new roads; cutting down or planting more trees; and existing trees will grow taller.

Busy Beaver Construction Co.

Reading Focus Tell students to look as they read for a *summary* paragraph that will help them answer the Reading Focus question. They can add important details from the *resource* to expand their responses.

1. Get Ready

Vocabulary
Support Terms dam, lodge, soil

Background
- The beaver is the largest rodent in North America. An adult is 90–120 cm (3–4 feet) long and weighs about 27 kg (60 lbs). Largely aquatic, beavers require clean water in which to build dams and lodges. After building these structures, they apply a "mortar" of mud to cement the logs and sticks together. Beavers guided much of the early exploration of the western United States. The search for beavers, prized for their fur, led trappers and explorers into new territory.

Discussion Starter
- **How do you think beaver dams affect other living things?** Encourage speculation. Possible responses: dams create ponds for fish to live in; birds have to find new homes when beavers chew down their trees; the size or speed of a stream may change and the animals or people downstream may not have enough water.

2. Guide the Discussion

Choose from the following strategies to facilitate discussion.

Making Comparisons
- **How are the beavers' changes similar to people's changes to the environment? How are the beavers' changes different?** Beavers and people both make changes in order to build homes for themselves. Sometimes people's changes provide homes for other living things, as beavers' changes do, but more often people's changes eliminate homes for plants and animals.

Busy Beaver Construction Co.

Reading Focus How do beavers change the environment, and how do the changes affect other living things?

People build dams to control the flow of water from rivers and streams. The beavers of North America, without any training in construction, or building, do the same thing. These hard-working animals build dams and keep them in repair.

Timber!
Beavers do a lot of work to build a dam. They use their sharp teeth to chew away at the trunks of trees. Beavers can chomp through a tree trunk 1 m (3 ft) thick! The trees come crashing down. Then the beavers cut the trunks and branches into logs, again using their sharp teeth. They float the logs into position in the stream. Then they cement the logs together with mud, stones, and leaves.

A Warm, Dry Lodge
Beavers build dams across the moving waters of streams and rivers. The dams create ponds. In the still water of the ponds, beavers build their habitat—a lodge. A lodge is a small living area made of tree parts and mud. The lodge rises up from the pond. The lodge protects a group of beavers from cold weather and from predators.

A Home for Others
The ponds created by dams become homes for other animals, too. Many kinds of fish as well as insects, spiders, frogs, and salamanders live in the quiet ponds. Water birds build nests near the ponds. Many of these animals would not be able to make their homes in streams that lacked dams.

dam

Science & Social Studies

USING MAPS

What to Do Students can locate states on an outline map with places that are named after beavers, such as Beaver, Oklahoma; Beaver Falls, Pennsylvania; Beaver Dam, Kentucky; Beaver City, Nebraska; Beaver Creek, Colorado; and Beaverton, Oregon. Suggest that they try to find other states having towns with similar names.

What's the Result? Ask students why they think people chose to name their towns in this way.

A Changed Place

Beavers cut down many trees along the shore to build their dams and lodges. When the beavers have cut down most of the trees near the pond, they move. They leave behind the results of their hard work and start all over again.

Over time, the ponds created by beaver dams fill with rich soil. They become beautiful meadows. Plants such as grasses and wildflowers grow in the meadows. By cutting down trees, building dams, creating ponds, and making lodges, beavers greatly change the environment. ■

The beavers enter their lodge through an underwater tunnel. ▼

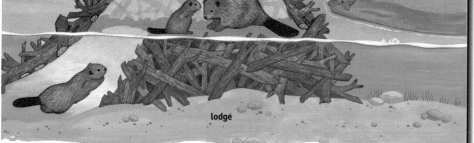

lodge

E63

Science & the Arts

MAKING MODELS

What to Do Invite students to make a small dam of sticks and mud (clay). They might also construct a running stream by putting soil and water in a large, tilted pan or work outside with a real stream. Then they can attempt to block the flow of water with a dam, as beavers do.

What's the Result? What did you learn about building dams with sticks and mud? Students probably have gained more respect for beavers' engineering skills. **What are some ways that a beaver dam can interfere with other animals' lives?** A dam can prevent fish from migrating, dry up or reduce the flow of the stream down river, flood animals' homes, drown plants, and destroy trees.

• **How are beavers' homes like yours? How are they different?** Both shelters are designed to provide their inhabitants with protection from the weather, and a place to store food and rear their young. People's homes may be built from natural materials like the beaver lodges, but they may also be constructed from other materials. Beaver lodges are built over water. People's homes are often built near a source of fresh water.

Connecting to the Activities

• *My Neighborhood Keeps Changing! pp. E60–E61*

• **In the activity, you learned that people can cause changes in a neighborhood. How do beavers change their neighborhoods?** They cut down trees and build dams that cause pools to form in rivers and streams. **How do these changes affect the other living things in the environment?** The beavers' changes provide homes and food for many living things, including fish and other water animals. The dam could also flood animal homes.

Meeting Individual Needs

Gifted and Talented Students might enjoy researching the impact of the beaver fur trade on the exploration of the western United States. They can share the results of the investigation through an oral report.

Multi-Age Classroom Students can work together in small groups to complete this activity. For example, those who are adept at drawing can create posters to illustrate the oral report. Create a learning center around the topic and provide resources of varying difficulty so that each student can find materials on his or her reading level.

3. Assess Understanding

Have students work in small groups to make drawings showing ways living things can change the environment and affect other living things within it. Have the groups present their drawings with an explanation to the class.

Reading Focus Answer

Beavers cut down trees and build dams, which create ponds. The ponds become homes for other animals and plants. The animals that lived in the trees must find other trees to live in.

People Change the Environment

Reading Focus As students read page E65, have them **compare and contrast** how people impact the wetlands.

1. Get Ready

Vocabulary
Science Terms ecosystem, wetlands
Support Terms swamps, marshes

Background
- In the mid-1800s, the U.S. government gave away 65 million acres of wetlands and encouraged people to drain and fill them as a prevention against mosquitoes. By 1980, half of the nation's 200 million acres of wetlands had been destroyed. Now research shows that wetlands help with flood control and filter farm wastes and other pollutants out of surface water. Three-quarters of the bird species in the United States, along with many fish and shellfish species, depend on the wetlands.

Discussion Starter
- **How do you think Earth looked before people began making changes?** Possible responses: there were no houses, buildings, roads or bridges; there were more forests, plants, open areas, birds, and other animals.

2. Guide the Discussion

Choose from the following strategies to facilitate discussion.

Connecting to the Activities
- *My Neighborhood Keeps Changing! pp. E60–E61*
- **Are there any parks or other areas in your neighborhood that help protect animals and plants?** Help students become more aware of the ecosystems in their community and local efforts to protect plants and animals.

People Change the Environment

Reading Focus How can changes people make to the wetlands be helpful and harmful?

What would the world look like without the changes people have made? There would be no buildings, no streets, and no highways. What else would be different?

The activity on pages E60 and E61 shows old and new pictures of a neighborhood. The changes were caused by the activities of people.

Too Wet

A place where living and nonliving things interact is called an **ecosystem**. Sometimes people change an ecosystem because they want to use land for farming or to build on. But not all land is suitable for these purposes. For example, some land may be too wet.

Science in Literature

Piranhas and Other Wonders of the Jungle
by Q. L. Pearce
Illustrated by Mary Ann Fraser
Julian Messner, 1990

KILLER ANTS MARCH!
"One of the most frightful creatures in Central Africa is less than one inch long. Feared by humans and animals alike, it is the driver ant. In a single colony, there may be up to 20 million biting ants, and once they have begun their march, nothing in their path is safe."

Read about how these dreaded ants are used to help people in the book *Piranhas and Other Wonders of the Jungle* by Q. L. Pearce.

E64

Science & Writing

WRITING BOOKS

What to Do *A Walk in the Rainforest* by Kristin Joy Pratt (Dawn Publications, 1992) is a colorful A–to–Z guide describing the rainforest. It was written and illustrated as a high school independent study project. After reading this book, students might enjoy working in small groups to write and illustrate their own A–to–Z lists of living things found in a wetland, desert, forest, or meadow environment.

What's the Result? Encourage groups to describe how the living things they drew have had to adapt to the changes people have made in the environment.

Building on wetlands is an example of a change that people have made to an ecosystem. **Wetlands** include swamps, marshes, and bogs. People drain the water from wetlands to use the land for farming, housing, and industry. Today, less than half the wetlands in the United States remain.

The wetlands are home to birds, insects, fish, snakes, beavers, and a large variety of plants. When people change wetland environments, many living things may lose their homes.

Making Things Better

People also make changes that improve their environments. Many people are working together to protect the world's wetlands. Some people even fill wetlands with water during long periods of dry weather.

People create new parks in which animals and plants are protected. They plant trees and gardens that become new homes for many different living things. In many ways, people are always changing the natural environment. ■

 Giants Stadium in New Jersey (left) was built on wetlands. The Everglades are wetlands in Florida (right). The original 48 states contained a total of 215 million acres of wetlands. Only 95 million acres remain. How many acres of wetlands have been lost?

E65

Integrating the Sciences

EARTH SCIENCE

What to Do Students can investigate how the environment can be changed by natural phenomena, such as volcanic eruptions, hurricanes, exceptionally hot or cold weather, glaciers, forest fires, droughts, and floods. They might work in small groups, each member researching a different phenomenon and the ways it affects the living things in an environment.

What's the Result? Both people and natural phenomena can change an environment. Which do you think causes the most damage? Why do you think so? Help students recognize that some human changes occur too quickly and are too drastic to allow the environment to adapt. As a result, habitats cannot recover and many plants and animals become extinct.

 Meeting Individual Needs

For Extra Help Have students work in groups to design posters focusing on preserving an environment, such as a prairie, forest, or wetland. Ask them to include the effects of human change on that environment, ways we can protect that environment, and reasons why we should protect it.

Identifying and Solving Problems

- **Since people often need to change the environment, how can we protect other living things?** Possible responses: make only changes that are really necessary, replace trees that are cut down with seedlings, prevent oil and chemical spills, protect the environments of endangered species, and so on.

 ## Science in Literature

Piranhas and Other Wonders of the Jungle
by Q. L. Pearce

After students read the book, have them work in small groups to compile lists of benefits that people can receive from jungles and rain forests. You may want to have them begin with p. 53 to list the benefits from the killer ants, and then divide up the remaining chapters among the groups.

 Students should indicate that 120 million acres of wetlands have been lost.

3. Assess Understanding

Students can work in groups of three or four to suggest ways people can protect existing plants and animals in the community and encourage new ones to live there. Provide time for groups to share their recommendations.

Reading Focus Answer

Draining and building on wetlands can cause living things to lose their homes. Filling dry wetlands with water and creating new parks helps to protect and create homes for living things.

Bringing Back the Buffaloes

Reading Focus Have students *use the graphic* (timeline) to identify the *causes* of the buffalo decline and the *effects* of conservation efforts.

1. Get Ready

Vocabulary
Support Terms bison, prairies, extinct

Discussion Starter
• **The song "Home on the Range" includes the line, "Give me a home where the buffalo roam...." Why do you think buffaloes no longer roam throughout the United States?** Encourage speculation. Ask students who have seen buffaloes to describe them.

2. Guide the Discussion

 Meeting Individual Needs

Students Acquiring English Help students understand the chronological aspect of a time line and practice using time-related words such as *before, after,* and *then.*

3. Assess Understanding

Students can work in groups of three or four to brainstorm an answer to the following question: **If people had never killed any buffaloes, would they still roam the Great Plains in large herds? Why or why not?** The changes people have made to the environment would have indirectly caused the death of great numbers of buffaloes.

Reading Focus Answer

Buffaloes almost disappeared because people killed them and changed their ecosystem. Their numbers increased once laws were passed to protect them.

 RESOURCE

Bringing Back the Buffaloes

Reading Focus What caused buffaloes to nearly disappear, and why have their numbers increased?

 TIME Capsule

Long ago the Great Plains of the United States and Canada were covered with large roaming herds of American bison, also called buffaloes. But the large herds of buffaloes began to disappear. And so did the prairies, or grasslands, they once roamed.

People changed much of the prairie land to make it suitable for building and farming.

But today, even without their old prairie land, the buffaloes are back in growing numbers. Take a trip back in time to find out why the buffaloes almost disappeared and how they've come back.

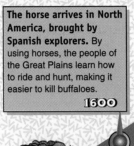

The horse arrives in North America, brought by Spanish explorers. By using horses, the people of the Great Plains learn how to ride and hunt, making it easier to kill buffaloes.
1600

All buffaloes east of the Mississippi River have been killed.
1800

1880
Hundreds of hunters wipe out the buffaloes of the Canadian plains.

E66

Science & Social Studies

IDENTIFYING

What to Do Explain that buffaloes were essentially a grocery store for Native Americans who lived on the plains. Besides using the meat for food, they used hides to make winter clothing and tepees. Sinews were used to make bowstrings; hair became ropes; the stomach became a water jug; and the bones were made into knives and other tools. Glue was made from boiled hooves, while the fat was used in soap. The horns became cups and spoons.

What's the Result? How did the near extinction of the buffaloes affect the Native Americans living on the plains? Students may say that killing the buffaloes eliminated a major resource on which Native Americans depended.

Several thousand buffaloes are moved to Wood Buffalo National Park in Alberta, Canada.

1920

1990s
Because they are protected, buffaloes are no longer in danger of becoming extinct.

1894
The buffalo is nearly extinct.
Theodore Roosevelt, who would later become President of the United States, wants to protect the buffalo. Congress passes a law against killing buffaloes. The herds slowly begin to grow again.

According to the National Bison Association, there are over 200,000 buffaloes in the United States. In Canada, the total number of buffaloes is expected to reach 120,000 by the year 2000.

Today, most buffaloes are in parks because the prairie land they once roamed has been changed. Farmland, factories, towns, and roads have replaced much of the old prairies. ◼

INVESTIGATION 1 WRAP-UP

REVIEW **1.** Explain how an animal can change its environment. Explain how people change their environments.

2. Give three examples of wetlands.

CRITICAL THINKING **3.** You observe that a large part of a tropical rain forest has been cut down. How might such a change affect the living things in that area? Explain your answer.

4. Give an example of two living things that have different habitats but live in the same ecosystem.

E67

Assessment

Portfolio

In My Opinion Invite students to select a recent change in their neighborhood or community and explain whether they think this change will help or harm living things in the environment. They might write a brief editorial to the local newspaper expressing their opinions.

Investigation Review ▶
Use Investigation Review p. 118 in the *Teacher Resource Book*.

Investigation Review

Name _____ Date _____

Look at the picture. Then answer the questions below.

1. What changes are taking place that improve the environment?
planting flowers and putting up a birdhouse

2. What changes are taking place that harm the environment?
littering, car exhaust

3. There is an area in your neighborhood that has become polluted. People have dumped old tires, aluminum cans, and other trash in the area. What are some things you can do to help make the area a better environment for all the living things in the neighborhood?
Some acceptable answers are to pick up the trash, haul away the tires, collect and recycle the cans, plant new flowers or shrubs.

Process Skills
Predicting
You are walking along a stream and you see some new arrivals to the area—beavers. Predict what will happen to the plant life in the area. Write your answer on a separate sheet of paper.

The beavers will cut down the trees along the stream to build their dams and lodges. Animals and plants that live in still water will begin to appear here. Other animals and plants may disappear.

Close
the Investigation

INVESTIGATION WRAP-UP

REVIEW
1. Possible answers: Beavers can build dams that form ponds and provide homes for other animals; buffaloes and other animals can change land by grazing. People can cut down trees, dig or fill ponds, dam rivers, build houses and roads, kill animals, and drain wetlands.

2. Wetlands include swamps, marshes, and bogs.

CRITICAL THINKING
3. The trees and small plants that grow on the forest floor are gone. The animals, birds, and insects that depended on them for homes, protection from predators, and food might die or be forced to go live someplace else. *(Evaluating, Applying, Expressing Ideas)*

4. Possible response: A bird and a squirrel both live in the same tree in the same forest but a squirrel lives in the trunk of the tree and the bird lives in a nest. *(Synthesizing, Applying, Expressing Ideas)*

CHALLENGE

Have students bring in photographs of their neighborhood or community that were taken five or more years ago. Encourage them to describe changes that have occurred and explain who or what caused these changes.

FOLLOWING UP

Baseline Assessment Return to the class pictures showing helpful and harmful changes that can take place in an environment. Encourage students to update the changes based on what they've learned in the investigation and to identify the causes of these changes.

Reteaching Have students work individually or in pairs to draw one of the environments discussed in this investigation before and after people made changes. Have them describe how the changes have affected living things.

Use *Science Notebook,* TRB p. 63.

Start
the Investigation

How Are Living Things Adapted to Their Environments?

pages E68–E76

Planner

Subconcept Living things have adaptations that enable them to cope with changes in their environment.

Objectives

- **Experiment** to find out how feathers help birds adapt to changing temperatures.
- **Describe** ways that plants and animals cope with changing temperatures.

Pacing 2–3 class periods

Science Terms migrate, hibernation, dormancy

Activate Prior Knowledge

Baseline Assessment Ask: **What are some things plants and animals can do when seasons change?** Save a list for Following Up.

How Are Living Things Adapted to Their Environments?

Why do you sweat when your environment is hot and shiver when it's cold? These are examples of adaptations. In Investigation 2, discover other ways living things are adapted to their environments.

Activity

Keeping Heat In

Adaptations help living things survive. In this activity find out how some animals are adapted to cold weather.

MATERIALS
- 2 large plastic jars
- 2 small plastic jars
- down feathers
- hot tap water
- 2 thermometers
- timer
- *Science Notebook*

SAFETY //////
Clean up spills immediately.

Procedure

1. In this activity, you'll **make models** of two animals. One has feathers. The other one does not. **Talk with your group** and **predict** which animal model will lose more heat in 30 minutes. **Record** your prediction in your *Science Notebook*.

2. Make a chart like the one shown.

Time (in min)	Temperature (°C) Model With Feathers	Temperature (°C) Model Without Feathers
0		
15		
30		

E68

Activity Keeping Heat In

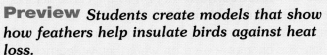

Preview *Students create models that show how feathers help insulate birds against heat loss.*

1. Get Ready

 GROUPS OF 4–6   **30 MINUTES**

Key Science Process Skills make and use models, control variables, predict, measure, record, hypothesize.

Meeting Individual Needs

INCLUSION

To ensure that students understand that their models represent birds, encourage them to add eyes, beaks, and other features to their jars. As they are adding each part, have them describe its function. Encourage them to classify parts according to those that help a bird eat, those that help it move, and those that do both.

LOGICAL/MATHEMATICAL

3. To make your models, place a small jar in a larger jar. Place down feathers around the small jar. Cover the sides of the small jar completely with feathers but don't pack the feathers tightly.

4. Place another small jar in a different larger jar. Don't put anything around this small jar.

5. Fill each small jar halfway with hot tap water. Take care not to wet the feathers. Put a thermometer in each small jar. Measure the temperature of the water in each jar. Record your readings under the correct heading on the first line in your chart.

Step 5

 See **SCIENCE** and **MATH TOOLBOX** page H8 if you need to review **Using a Thermometer.**

6. After 15 minutes, record the temperature of the water in each jar. Wait another 15 minutes. Then record both temperatures again.

Analyze and Conclude

1. By how many degrees did the temperature in each jar change?

2. Which animal model lost more heat? How does this result compare with your prediction?

3. Study your models. Hypothesize about how down feathers help a bird stay warm.

 Technology
Link
CD-ROM

INVESTIGATE FURTHER!

Use the **Best of the Net—Science CD-ROM**, Life Sciences, *Bristlecone Pine* to find out about the discovery of ancient bristlecone pine trees, the oldest living things on Earth. Find out how growth rings reveal changes in Earth's environment.

E69

 Technology **CD-ROM**
Link

INVESTIGATE FURTHER!

Students can use the **Best of the Net–Science CD-ROM** Life Sciences, *Bristlecone Pine* to investigate the ancient bristlecone pine trees, the oldest living things on Earth. Students learn about Earth's oldest living inhabitant, "Methuselah" a bristlecone tree that is 4,725 years old and has lived more than a millennium longer than any other tree. Students discover how these trees were found and where they live. They learn about adaptations that have allowed the trees to survive for so many years. Students can complete an activity in which they answer questions about tree ring dating and the preservation of old trees.

Multi-Age Strategy Students who are adept at measuring could assist others with their measurements.

Materials Hints Use 32- and 12-oz. jars for best results. About 0.25 oz. of feathers will be required for each model. Use sterilized feathers to prevent spreading disease. They are available at most craft stores.

Safety Review safety precautions with students. Clean up any spills immediately. Remind students to be careful when handling glass thermometers.

2. Guide the Procedure

- If possible, students might place feathers across the opening of the small jar, too. For best results, water should be 45–50°C (113–122°F).

- Have students describe the limitations of this model compared to a real bird.

 Have students record predictions and measurements and answer questions on *Science Notebook,* TRB, pp. 64–65.

Science Processor Have students use the CD-ROM Spreadsheet and Grapher to organize and display their data.

3. Assess Performance

Process Skills Checklist
- Did students **predict** which model would lose more heat? Were their predictions based on an understanding that feathers serve the same function to birds as warm clothing does to humans?

- Did students correctly **make and use models** of animals with and without feathers?

- Did students **measure** the temperature of the water in each jar accurately? Did they indicate temperatures in degrees Celsius?

- Did students accurately **collect and record data** as to which animal lost more heat?

- Did students **hypothesize** that feathers help an animal retain heat?

Analyze and Conclude
1. Exact measurements will vary, but the temperature in the jar surrounded by feathers should change less than the temperature in the other jar.

2. The animal model without feathers lost more heat. This should match student predictions.

3. Feathers help a bird stay warm by holding in heat.

RESOURCE

Beating the Heat

Reading Focus Give students a head start at answering the Reading Focus question by asking them to *preview* the resource. Have them read each section heading and the first one or two sentences.

1. Get Ready

Vocabulary

Support Terms adaptations, overheating, perspiration, sweat, burrows, moisture, saguaro

Background

- Deserts cover approximately one-fifth of Earth. The largest are the Sahara in Africa and the Great Desert of Australia. Most deserts receive less than ten inches of rainfall per year. As a result, desert plants are adapted to prevent water loss through evaporation; leaves are slender or nonexistent. The plant body is often fleshy, storing large amounts of water that protect the plant from the heat, and may serve as a water source for desert animals.

- Desert animals have many interesting adaptations. The dune lizard "dances" by raising its alternate fore and hind legs. This allows the sand under it to cool down. Then the lizard will lie on its stomach with all four legs and its tail in the air to cool off its appendages. A camel will often stand with its hump facing the Sun. The hump, which is made up of body fat, absorbs the Sun's rays and thereby protects the vital organs of the camel. The hump also provides a large shady spot for other animals.

- An oasis is an area within a desert with enough water to support vegetation. Some oases are large enough to support cities and agriculture.

RESOURCE

Beating the Heat

Reading Focus How are different plants and animals adapted to desert environments?

Both animals and plants have adaptations that protect them from extreme heat. On a blazing hot day in summer, what do you do to stay cool? To protect your skin from burning in the sunlight and your body from overheating, you'd likely head for a shady spot.

Your body has a built-in way of cooling down. In hot weather your skin becomes covered with tiny droplets of perspiration, or sweat. The ability to sweat is an adaptation that helps prevent overheating. When sweat dries up, the drying process cools your skin.

Although sweating is an important adaptation to humans, few other animals sweat. In a desert, if an animal did sweat, it would quickly become dried out. There is little water available in the desert to replace the body's lost moisture.

Life in the Desert

How does a desert animal, which lives where the Sun scorches the sand all day, survive? There are no tall leafy trees for shade. In some deserts, daytime air temperatures can reach 55°C (131°F). Rain is scarce, and there are few water holes to drink from. Deserts may seem to be impossible places to live in. But, amazingly, the world's deserts are home to thousands of kinds of plants and animals. All have adaptations to "beat the heat."

Using Math *In the Namib Desert in Africa, shown here, surface temperatures can reach as high as 77°C (170°F). Compare this temperature to the daytime air temperature in the desert, given in the text above.*

E70

Science & Literature

DESERT STUDY

What to Do Students might enjoy reading *Cactus Hotel* by Brenda Guiberson (Holt, 1991) or a similar book about ways animals adapt to extreme temperatures. The book describes the life cycle of the saguaro cactus and emphasizes its role as a home for various forms of desert wildlife.

What's the Result? Students could prepare a class mural showing how the different plants and animals adapt to the desert. Then they could identify similarities and differences among the adaptations. Guide students to recognize that the adaptations help the plants and animals survive under difficult conditions.

Insects Keep Cool

Some desert insects have body designs that keep them cool. One little beetle that lives in the Namib Desert of southwestern Africa survives by keeping its body away from the hot sand. How does it do this? Nicknamed the stilt beetle, this insect "tiptoes" over sun-baked sand dunes on long stiltlike legs.

The black color of some beetles can be a problem in the desert. This is because dark-colored material heats faster than does light-colored material. Many desert beetles have white or yellow wax covering their dark bodies. The light-colored wax reflects sunlight, keeping the insect's body cool. Because wax is waterproof, the waxy covering also helps hold in moisture, keeping the beetle from drying out.

What characteristics of a stilt beetle help it survive in the desert?

E71

DESIGNING

What to Do People around the world adapt to hot temperatures in different ways. Encourage students to look for magazine pictures that show how people keep cool in dry desert areas and in humid rainforest areas. If it's hot outside now, invite students to try out some of the techniques they learn about.

What's the Result? Challenge students to arrange their pictures in a design that shows techniques used in dry areas, those used in humid areas, and those that overlap. **In what ways do you think the high temperatures in some parts of the world affect people's lives?** Climate affects the type of clothing people wear, their homes, jobs, food, recreation, and so on.

Discussion Starter

- **How do you stay cool on a hot day?** Possible responses: go swimming, wear lighter clothing, stay in the shade, drink cool liquids, or stay in air-conditioned buildings.

- **Which of these things can animals do?** Possible responses: some animals can stay in the shade, swim, and drink water; some pets can stay in an air conditioned environment.

- **Which can plants do?** Students should recognize that plants are not able to do any of the activities humans or other animals do.

- **In what other ways do you suppose plants and animals protect themselves from hot temperatures?** Encourage speculation. Possible answers include animals burrowing into the ground to avoid the hot sun and conserve moisture and plants with root systems designed to reach water or store water in their tissues. Both may enter a period of dormancy: plants as seeds; animals may sleep during the day and forage at night when it is cooler.

2. Guide the Discussion

Choose from the following strategies to facilitate discussion.

Connecting to the Activities
- *Keeping Heat In, pp. E68–E69*
- **In the activity, you found out that feathers help keep a bird warm. Why would birds that live in the hot desert need feathers?** Students might suggest that feathers can help keep heat away from a bird's body. Light-color feathers would reflect the sunlight.

Thinking Critically
- **Would you be likely to see an earthworm in the desert? Why or why not?** No, at least not anywhere near the surface. A worm's moist skin would allow too much water to evaporate. It would also be burned if it crawled across the hot sand.

 The surface temperature given for the Namib Desert is 22°C (39°F) higher than that given in the text.

Making Inferences

- **During what time of day do you think most desert animals (predators) hunt? Why?** They would hunt at night because that is when more small animals (prey) would be active.

Drawing Conclusions

- **Do you think a kangaroo rat would be healthier if it lived in a place with a lot of water nearby? Why or why not?** No. This rat has adapted to limited water and probably would not benefit if more were available.

 Meeting Individual Needs

Students Acquiring English Encourage students to consult a map of the world that shows climates. Have them list the names of countries where plants and animals would have adaptations for high temperatures. Assign students a country and have them do research to find an example of one plant and one animal with such adaptations. These would include countries that have desert lands, such as Saudi Arabia and Australia.

Gifted and Talented Make available reference books on plants and animals for students to consult. Have them choose a plant or animal to draw as it presently appears in its environment. Then have them draw how they think it might appear a million years from now. Have students write a story to accompany the pictures explaining how conditions changed in the environment and how the plant or animals adapted to new conditions.

Never Thirsty

The behaviors of desert animals are also adaptations to the hot, dry environment. Kangaroo rats have some unusual adaptations for conserving water. A kangaroo rat may go its entire life without ever taking a drink of water! Kangaroo rats get moisture from the food they eat—seeds, juicy grasses, and the pulp of cactus plants. These animals don't sweat, and they are active only at night.

 Internet Field Trip
Visit **www.eduplace.com** to find out how desert animals have adapted to their dry environments.

▲ A kangaroo rat burrows in the sand to stay cool during the day.

The saguaro cactus grows in deserts of the southwestern U.S. and northern Mexico. ▼

E72

Science, Technology & Society

GLOBAL WARMING

What to Do Ask students to share what they know about global warming. Explain that some scientists think air temperatures around the world are slowly getting warmer because air pollution is trapping the Sun's heat near Earth's surface. Other scientists think the loss of ozone in the upper atmosphere, also caused by air pollution, is allowing any extra heat to escape into space.

What's the Result? Have students list ways they think warmer temperatures might affect plants and animals worldwide. Guide students to recognize that animals can usually go some place cooler, but plants cannot move. If plants die, the animals that eat them will starve.

During the day, kangaroo rats sleep sealed inside their "cool" burrows. Their burrows are about 0.3 m (1 ft) below the desert sand. Since the Sun doesn't heat this sand directly, the temperature in the burrow is a cool 30°C (86°F).

Hidden Water

Plants also have adaptations to the hot, dry desert environment. Cactus plants hold a lot of water inside. They have thick stems and slender, spiny leaves that keep in moisture. Cactus roots are widespread just beneath the desert's surface. These shallow roots can rapidly take in water from a rare desert rainfall before the sunlight causes the water to dry up. Then the water is stored for weeks inside the cactus.

The largest kind of cactus is the saguaro (sə gwär′ō). After years of growing slowly, a saguaro can reach 15 m (50 ft) in height and can store hundreds of liters of water. ■

A flowering saguaro cactus ▼

UNIT PROJECT LINK

Another environment that you have read about in this unit is the tropical rain forest. Tropical rain forests have many important resources. Find out why tropical rain forests are disappearing. Make a poster that lists things you and your friends can do to help save the rain forests.

Technology Link

For more help with your Unit Project, go to **www.eduplace.com**.

E73

UNIT PROJECT LINK

Students may wish to review the chapters on "Nature's Medicine Chest" and the "Future of the Rain Forests" in *Piranhas and Other Wonders of the Jungle* before beginning this project link. Students should work in small groups, researching different aspects of the rain forest, and should brainstorm ideas to include on the posters. Encourage students to take notes on *Science Notebook,* TRB, p. 66. Then have students use Unit Project Masters 5–6 (TRB pp. 20–21) to research their information.

Technology Link

Visit **www. eduplace.com** for a scoring rubric to assess students' progress and to share students' results on-line.

Thinking Critically

- **What do you think would happen to desert plants if the area where they lived had large amounts of rainfall several years in a row?** They would not conserve as much water. Their root systems might stop growing or grow deeper. Students might realize that other, competing plants might begin to grow if more water became available.

Drawing Conclusions

- **What might happen if all the plants on Earth needed the same amount of water to survive?** Some areas would have no plants because there was too little or too much water. Those areas would also have no animals because animals depend on plants (and plant-eating animals) for food.

3. Assess Understanding

Students can work in small groups to make desert wildlife flashcards out of index cards. On one side of each card, have them draw a different desert plant, animal, or insect. On the opposite side, have them list the ways that the organism protects itself from heat. Students can take turns looking at the pictures and recalling each living thing's adaptations to the desert environment.

Reading Focus Answer

Beetles "tiptoe" on long legs to keep their bodies away from hot sand. Their bodies are covered by light-colored wax, which helps keep them cool and moist. Kangaroo rats are only active during the cool of night and rely on the food they eat rather than drinking for moisture. Cactus plants hold a lot of water; they have thick stems and spiny leaves that keep in moisture.

Internet Field Trip

From **www.eduplace.com** students can link to a Web site on desert animals. A trip log will guide their visit to the site.

When the Going Gets Tough...

Reading Focus Have students **look for main ideas** as they read each section of the resource. They can then use the main ideas to construct a *summary* that will help answer the Reading Focus question.

1. Get Ready

Vocabulary
Science Terms migrate, hibernation, dormancy
Additional Term cycles

Background
• Hibernation is a protective adaptation that allows many animals to survive freezing temperatures. During hibernation, stored body fat is used as fuel to maintain vital functions. No growth occurs, and metabolic and physical activities are minimal. Animals that metabolically control their body temperatures must find sheltered environments. Most of their stored energy is used to keep warm. Animals such as frogs and fish hibernate by assuming the temperature of their surroundings. To avoid freezing, they retreat to water below the frost line, where temperatures remain warmer. Scientists hypothesize that biorhythms, or cyclical changes in an animal's physiology and activity, govern hibernation and migration. Stimuli such as shorter days and cooler temperatures tell the animal to settle in for the winter or head south.

Discussion Starter
• **When winter is coming, what changes in nature do you notice?** Possible responses: leaves change color and fall, birds fly south, squirrels gather and store food.

• **Why do you think these things happen as cold weather approaches?** Students might respond that these changes help the living things prepare for colder temperatures.

Reading Focus What adaptations do some plants and animals have to survive cold winters?

Maple trees drop their leaves, robins fly south, and woodchucks curl up in dens and go into a deep sleep. These things all happen as the cold of winter approaches. Why?

In nature there are many cycles—summer and winter, rainy season and dry season, and others. These natural cycles happen in different places around the world. Sometimes a cycle creates big changes in the environment. Then plants and animals have to change in some way, too, in order to survive.

Winter Travel

How can an animal survive through a cold, snowy winter if it can't find enough food to eat? One way is for the animal to **migrate** (mī′grāt), or travel to a warmer place where it can find food.

Many kinds of birds migrate. It's not the cold weather that makes them leave. The activity on pages E68 and E69 shows that feathers help birds stay warm. Some birds can survive cold weather if they can find enough food.

The lesser golden plover and the Arctic tern are two kinds of birds that migrate. ▼

equator

▲ **Lesser golden plover**

E74

Science & the Arts

ILLUSTRATING

What to Do Students might enjoy making flip books that illustrate an animal's preparation for hibernation or a bird's migration. Encourage them to include the environmental changes that trigger these animal behaviors. Provide time for students to share and compare their books.

What's the Result? Why might the same environmental change cause one animal to prepare to hibernate and another animal to start migrating? Animals are adapted to their environment and their own needs. Their instincts tell them what to do.

Multi-Age Classroom Some students may simply draw one picture showing an animal preparing to migrate or hibernate. Whatever the level, make sure each student's work is recognized.

Some seed-eating birds, such as blue jays and cardinals, don't migrate.

But insect-eating birds and birds whose food is often covered by snow or ice usually migrate before winter comes. Some fly long distances. The lesser golden plover migrates over 3,200 km (2,000 mi)—from Alaska to Hawaii. And the Arctic tern migrates about 20,000 km (12,000 mi)—from the Arctic in the north to the Antarctic in the south!

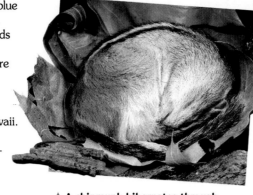

▲ A chipmunk hibernates through most of the winter but may wake up on warmer days to eat.

◄ Arctic tern

Winter Sleep

How else do animals survive a cold winter without food? Some animals go into a deep sleep, called **hibernation** (hī bər nā'shən). Bears, ground squirrels, woodchucks, snakes, and bats all may hibernate during winter.

While an animal is in this deep sleep, its body temperature usually drops. Its heartbeat rate slows, and it breathes less. All these changes mean that an animal uses up less energy. Therefore, it can survive a long time without eating.

When warmer weather returns, the animal begins to warm up, too. Its heart starts beating faster, and soon it wakes up—to spring and a new supply of food!

E75

Science & Social Studies

MIGRATION

What to Do Have small groups investigate the migratory patterns of birds in the United States, using a bird guide as a resource. Have each group draw the paths that certain birds follow. Encourage students to note on maps which species commonly pass through their area.

What's the Result? What makes birds follow the migration paths they do? These paths are sources of food, safe places to rest, and favorable wind currents. **What kinds of things might people do to cause birds to change their migration paths?** They might clear fields and forests, fill ponds, drain wetlands, build houses and factories, and increase the air pollution.

2. Guide the Discussion

Choose from the following strategies to facilitate discussion.

Connecting to the Activities
- *Keeping Heat In, pp. E68–E69*
- **If feathers help keep birds warm, why do some birds need to migrate in the winter?** The cold weather and snow can kill or cover up the birds' food supply, such as insects. These birds migrate to warmer areas to get enough food to survive. Seed-eating birds, such as blue jays and cardinals, will not migrate because they can find seeds in the winter.

Making Comparisons
- **How are the ways that plants survive winter similar to animals' hibernation?** Both plants and hibernating animals slow their activity and live off stored food.

Transparency 26: Visual/Spatial Activity
Use the transparency "Migration of Gray Whales" to compare the migration of whales to the migration of birds.

3. Assess Understanding

 Groups of six can play "Adaptation ABCs." Let each group sit in a circle. The first student will name a plant or animal that starts with A and explain how it survives cold weather. For example: "A—I'm an antelope and I migrate." Go around the circle, having students give examples for as many letters of the alphabet as possible.

Meeting Individual Needs
Students Acquiring English As students play "Adaptation ABCs" (above), be ready to help students with limited vocabularies think of animal names. Make sure each group includes students who are fluent in English.

Reading Focus Answer

Birds have feathers to help keep them warm. To find food, some animals migrate to warmer places. To use less energy, some animals hibernate and some plants become dormant. Some trees lose their leaves and live off food stored in their roots.

Close the Investigation

INVESTIGATION WRAP-UP

REVIEW

1. Possible responses: Beetles "tiptoe" on long legs to keep their bodies away from hot sand and cactuses hold a lot of water to survive in the desert.

2. Hibernation is the deep sleep some animals go into and dormancy is a decrease in plant activity. Both allow living things to survive cold winters by slowing their activity and living off stored food.

CRITICAL THINKING

3. Birds that survive cold weather can fluff their feathers to decrease heat loss. They also eat seeds that can be found in the winter. The other birds have feathers, too, but they may eat food that is not available in winter, such as insects. They have adapted to the cold by migrating to more favorable environments. *(Analyzing, Applying, Expressing Ideas)*

4. People perspire in the heat, using the drying process to cool their skin. Desert animals can't perspire, because they would dry up and die without new water sources to replenish them. *(Analyzing, Synthesizing, Evaluating)*

CHALLENGE

Have students investigate how the migration of buffaloes on the Great Plains affected the movement of Native Americans during the 1800s.

FOLLOWING UP

Baseline Assessment Return to the list of students' responses of things that plants and animals can do when the temperature changes. Encourage students to update the list based on what they learned in the investigation. Remind them to include adaptations of animals, plants, and insects.

Reteaching Have students work independently or in pairs to make two word webs that center on heat and cold. Ask them to connect words and phrases to each web, describing adaptations that plants and animals have to these conditions.

 Use *Science Notebook*, TRB p. 67.

Plants in Winter

Plants are rooted to one spot, so they can't migrate. But their activities can slow, as if they were going into a deep sleep. This decrease in plant activity is called **dormancy** (dôr′mən sē). Plants become dormant during the winter.

As winter approaches, many trees—such as maples, oaks, poplars, elms, and chestnuts—lose their leaves. Without leaves, a tree can't make food. So, during dormancy the tree lives off food that is stored elsewhere in the plant—for example, in the roots.

Some plants, such as ferns, die above ground. But their roots survive underground through winter. When the weather warms up, the plants begin to grow again. ■

▲ Each autumn, trees like this maple lose their leaves.

INVESTIGATION 2 WRAP-UP

REVIEW **1.** Describe one adaptation of an animal and one adaptation of a plant for survival in the desert.

2. Compare hibernation and dormancy.

CRITICAL THINKING **3.** There is snow on the ground and on tree branches and bushes. You see only one or two kinds of birds. What adaptation do the birds have for keeping warm? Why did other kinds of birds leave?

4. What adaptation do you have to beat the heat? Do most desert animals have the same adaptation? Explain your answer.

E76

Assessment

Investigation Review

Name _____ Date _____

1. Circle the sentence about the desert animals that is **not** true.
 a. Stilt beetles keep cool by tiptoeing across the hot sand.
 b. Many desert animals sweat, which keeps them cool.
 c. A kangaroo rat may go its entire life without drinking water.
 d. The white wax on desert beetles reflects the sun and keeps in moisture.

2. Animals and plants have many different ways to deal with harsh environments or changes in their environments. Match the animal or plant on the left with its adaptation on the right. Then answer the question below.

 _d_ Arctic tern   **a.** hibernates in winter
 _c_ kangaroo rat   **b.** becomes dormant in winter
 _e_ cactus   **c.** stays in its cool burrow during the day
 _a_ woodchuck   **d.** migrates to a warmer climate
 _b_ oak tree   **e.** stores water in its thick stems

3. What special adaptation do you have to help you deal with hot summer weather?

I perspire, or sweat. When the drops of sweat dry, or
evaporate, my body becomes cooler.

Process Skills
Making a Model

What did making a model of a bird tell you about how a bird protects itself from the cold?

A bird's feathers hold in body heat and protect it from
the cold.

Performance

Debate Remind students that zoos depend on people visiting them to meet their expenses, feed the animals, and stay open. Have students debate whether zoos should prevent their birds from migrating and discourage their animals from hibernating during the winter.

◄ **Investigation Review**
Use Investigation Review p. 119 in the *Teacher Resource Book*.

REFLECT & EVALUATE

Word Power

Write the letter of the term that best completes each sentence.

1. Environments that include swamps, marshes, and bogs are ___.
2. To travel to a warmer place to find food is to ___.
3. A decrease in activity in plants during winter is called ___.
4. Some animals go into a deep winter sleep called ___.

a. dormancy
b. hibernation
c. migrate
d. wetlands

Check What You Know

Write the term in each pair that best completes each sentence.

1. When people change environments, many living things may lose their (adaptations, homes).
2. Sweating is an adaptation for keeping (wet, cool).
3. When food is scarce, some birds (migrate, hibernate).
4. While an animal hibernates, its heartbeat rate (slows down, speeds up).

Problem Solving

1. A family on vacation decides to go scuba diving. The group leader tells the family not to take any of the plants and animals from their underwater environment. Why is it important for the divers not to change the underwater environment?

2. Brown bears build up fat in their bodies before hibernating. How is this an adaptation?

Study the drawing. List all the ways that the beavers changed their environment. How did these changes affect other animals?

E77

Assessment

Chapter Test

Name _____ Date _____

Check What You Know Each item is worth 8 points.

For questions 1–4, circle the letter of the word or words that best complete each sentence.

1. People make changes that do not harm the environment when they ___.
   a. build large buildings
   b. plant trees and gardens
   c. drain wetlands
   d. build skyscrapers

2. A beaver changes the environment by ___.
   a. draining ponds
   b. digging up the soil
   c. building mounds
   d. damming up streams

3. One way living things have become adapted to the desert environment is by being able to ___.
   a. conserve water
   b. migrate
   c. perspire, or sweat
   d. grow trees

4. A(n) ___ is an animal that hibernates during the long, cold winter.
   a. Arctic tern
   b. kangaroo rat
   c. woodchuck
   d. deer

Word Power Each item is worth 7 points.

Write the letter of the term that best matches the definition.

_d_ 5. an environment made up of many grasses that is home to the American bison, or buffalo

_e_ 6. land that is soaked with water and is home to many birds, frogs, and other animals

_b_ 7. a deep sleep during winter for certain animals

_a_ 8. an environment that has little water and is usually hot during the day

_c_ 9. to move to a new area when the seasons change

a. desert
b. hibernation
c. migrate
d. prairie
e. wetland

Chapter Test

Name _____ Date _____

Problem Solving Each item is worth 15 points.

The Hoh Rain Forest is located in the state of Washington. The evergreen trees growing there are hundreds of years old and reach hundreds of meters into the sky. Some junglelike plants grow on the forest floor. Mosses hang from the branches and cover the tree trunks. Many different kinds of birds fly from branch to branch. Elk, black bears, mountain lions, and other animals roam throughout the forest.

10. Explain how cutting down all the trees would change the environment.

Cutting down all the trees would drastically alter the environment. Habitats would be destroyed, forcing forest animals to move or die. Accept all reasonable answers.

11. Make a hypothesis as to what might happen if only selected trees were cut. [HINT: Think about any positive changes that might occur.]

Removing selected trees would make open areas in the forest. These could stimulate growth of underbrush, providing new areas of shelter and food for living things. Accept all reasonable answers.

REFLECT & EVALUATE

Word Power

1. d   **2.** c   **3.** a   **4.** b

Check What You Know

1. homes   **2.** cool   **3.** migrate   **4.** slows down

Problem Solving

1. Changing the environment can alter or destroy the homes or food sources of the plants and animals, making it more difficult for them to survive.

2. The bears use this stored fat during hibernation to get the energy they need to survive the cold winter without food.

The beavers have cut down trees and built a dam that changes the flow of the stream or river. They have destroyed the homes of the animals in the trees and created new homes for animals in the water.

Assess Performance

Student Task

Have students look for ways people are changing the environment near their homes or school. Have them write about any changes they see and describe how these changes affect other living things.

Scoring Rubric

Points	What To Look For
3	Student thoroughly and clearly describes changes and their effects on other living things.
2	Student clearly describes changes but does not thoroughly describe their effects on other living things.
1	Student's description of changes and their effects on other living things is not thorough or stated clearly.

◄ **Chapter Test**
Use pp. 120–121 in the *Teacher Resource Book*.

UNIT E — Using READING SKILLS

Compare and Contrast

Review Reading Strategies

Have students turn to *Reading to Learn* on pp. S12–S13 to review the reading strategies.

Reinforce the Reading Skill

Ask a volunteer to read the lesson title on page E78 (*Compare and Contrast*). Reinforce that **compare** means "to show likeness" and **contrast** means "to show difference." Then have students take turns reading aloud the introductory paragraph and the tips in the notepad ("Look for these signal words . . ."). Explain that some signal words show likeness and other signal words show difference.

Model these strategies for comparing and contrasting.

- **Before Reading** Have students read the title and the first sentence in each paragraph. Ask students: **What two things are being compared?** (Plants are being compared to humans.)

- **While Reading** Point out the science terms. Explain that students should read the words around the high-lighted words to help them figure out their meanings. **What are producers?** (They are living things that produce their own food.) **What is a consumer?** (It is a living thing that gets its food from other living things.) Tell students to look for likeness and differences. Ask: **How are producers like or different from consumers?** (Producers produce their own food; consumers eat producers or other consumers.)

- **After Reading** Students should complete the exercise. (Suggested responses: *Producers include plants such as wheat, seaweed, and oats. Consumers include animals such as locusts, sea bass, and horses. Producers are eaten by consumers.*) If they are having trouble, encourage students to discuss their charts with a partner.

Apply the Reading Skill

Suggest that students can use these strategies for comparing and contrasting in the Resources.

UNIT E — Using READING SKILLS

Compare and Contrast

When you read, ask if two or more things, events, or ideas are being compared. Look for signal words that tell how things are alike and how they are different.

Read the paragraphs below. Then complete the exercise that follows.

> Look for these signal words to help you compare and contrast.
> - To show similar things: *like, the same as*
> - To show different things: *different from, by contrast*

What's for Dinner?

Plants make their own food inside their leaves. Plants take in water and air from their environment. The leaves soak up sunlight. Plants use the Sun's energy to make food from water and a gas in the air. This food can be stored in roots, leaves, and other plant parts for use later on. . . . Living things that can make their own food are called **producers**. Plants are producers.

Since your body can't produce its own food, as a plant does, you have to get it another way—by eating something else. That means that you are a consumer. A **consumer** is a living thing that eats plants, animals, or other living things.

Make a chart like the one shown. Compare and contrast producers and consumers by completing your chart.

Producers	Consumers

E78

Meeting Individual Needs

STUDENTS ACQUIRING ENGLISH

Help students understand the terms *compare* and *contrast* by clarifying the meanings of *same* and *different*. Include those terms students will encounter in the reading that reflect similarities and differences, such as *another way* and *something else*. Provide students with a Venn diagram (TRB p. 10) and label the outer circles *producer* and *consumer*. Have students list in the overlapping part of the circles qualities that producers and consumers share.

LINGUISTIC

Using MATH SKILLS

 Analyze Data

Some birds migrate very long distances. This table shows distances, in kilometers, that some birds migrate.

Migration Distances of Selected Birds	
Bird	**One-way Distance (km)**
Arctic tern	17,600
Atlantic brant	1,400
Barn swallow	9,600
Long-tailed jaeger	11,200
Pacific brant	4,000
Pacific golden plover	3,200
Snow goose	4,000
Whooping crane	4,800

Use the data in the table to complete the exercises.

1. Write the migration distances for these birds in order from shortest to longest.

2. Which of the birds listed migrates the longest distance? the shortest distance?

3. The arctic tern migrates for eight months each year. How many months is this bird not migrating?

4. How far does the whooping crane travel on a round-trip migration?

You may wish to use a calculator for Exercises 5 and 6.

5. How much longer is the round trip of the snow goose than the round trip of the Atlantic brant?

6. The Pacific brant migrates 4,000 km in three days. If the bird were to fly the same distance each day, how many kilometers would it fly in a day?

E79

Science & Math

ROUND-TRIP MIGRATION

What to Do Have students determine the round-trip migration distances for each bird listed in the table. They may wish to use calculators.

What's the Result? You might want students to compile their data in a table.

Using MATH SKILLS

UNIT E

 Analyze Data

Reinforce the Math Skill

Remind students that a table is a useful way to organize data. Have students look at the table on the pupil page. Point out the title of the table as well as the titles at the top of each column.

Apply the Math Skill

Explain to students that to find a particular bird's migration distance, they should find the correct row and then read across. Once you are certain that students understand how to read the table, have them complete the pupil page.

Answers

1. Atlantic brant, Pacific golden plover, snow goose and Pacific brant, whooping crane, barn swallow, long-tailed jaeger, Arctic tern.

2. The Arctic tern; the Atlantic brant

3. four months

4. 9,600 km

5. 5,200 km longer

6. Approximately 1,333.3 km in a day.

THINK LIKE A SCIENTIST

Before students begin with this page, you may want to have them review the steps in the scientific process. Refer students to pages S2–S11 and have them briefly summarize how they would apply the process as they complete the page. Then have them refer to their summaries as they proceed with the steps of the Unit Wrap-up.

WRITING IN SCIENCE

Model an outline format. Set minimum requirements for the research you want students to include.

Use these questions to evaluate student performance.

- Has the student researched sufficient information for the outline?
- Does the outline follow the format provided?
- Is information outlined logically?
- Are there at least two subheads for each main head?

UNIT PROJECT WRAP-UP

You may wish to have a class "Rain Forest Celebration Day," where students can display their mural and posters for other classes and family members to come and see. Have students prepare brief "jungle talks" about the information on their mural and posters. The talks might be about animal camouflage, layers of rain forest plant life, how natural or human damage affects a rain forest, important products of rain forests, or how people can help protect rain forests. Students could decorate the classroom like a rain forest and provide healthy, natural snacks such as nuts or fruit.

- For more information on how to wrap up the Unit Project, see pages E1o and E1p.
- For suggestions on how to assess the Unit Project, see Unit Project Scoring Rubric Master 7 (TRB p. 22).

UNIT **E** WRAP-UP!

On your own, use scientific methods to investigate a question about roles of living things.

THINK LIKE A SCIENTIST

Ask a Question

Pose a question about roles of living things that you would like to investigate. For example, ask, "How does temperature affect the activity of decomposers?"

Make a Hypothesis

Suggest a hypothesis that is a possible answer to the question. One hypothesis is that a low temperature slows the activity of decomposers.

Plan and Do a Test

Plan a controlled experiment to compare the action of decomposers at different temperatures. You could start with two samples of moldy bread, self-sealing sandwich bags, and a refrigerator. Develop a procedure that uses these materials to test the hypothesis. With permission, carry out your experiment. Follow the safety guidelines on pages S14–S15.

Record and Analyze

Observe carefully and record your data accurately. Make repeated observations.

Draw Conclusions

Look for evidence to support the hypothesis or to show that it is false. Draw conclusions about the hypothesis. Repeat the experiment to verify the results.

WRITING IN SCIENCE
Outline

Write an outline for a report on animal or plant adaptations. Research the information for your outline. Follow these guidelines for your outline.

- Write a title for your outline.
- Put Roman numerals (I, II, III) next to main ideas.
- Put capital letters (A, B) next to supporting details.
- Include three main heads with two details for each.

E80

Home–School Connection

The Closing Letter at the end of this unit suggests additional activities about living things that family members can do at home, as well as books students and their families can read together. Distribute the Closing Letter (TRB p. 6) to students at the end of this unit.

Closing Letter

Dear Family,

We hope that you and your student have enjoyed exploring the roles of living things. Would you like to learn more about how plants and animals are adapted to their environments? We invite you to try these ideas.

- Visit a zoo or a natural history museum. Compare and contrast adaptations that may help different animals get their food. Look especially at the ears, mouths, feet, and tails of the animals.
- Make up a plant or an animal that has an unusual method of protecting itself. What might happen if your plant or animal was threatened?
- Read all about it! The books below can help you learn more about the roles of living things.

Animal Homes: Burrows
by Shirley Greenway (Newington Press, 1991).
This well-researched and beautifully illustrated book explains how different animals build and use their burrows.

Birds of Prey
by John Bonnett Wexo (Creative Education, 1991).
This informative presentation, with detailed drawings and photographs, tells how the survival of some birds of prey is threatened.

Creepy Crawlies: Ladybugs, Lobsters & Other Amazing Arthropods
by Ruth Thompson (Sterling, 1991).
Fine illustrations supplement this clever introduction to the world of arthropods.

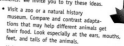

TEACHER NOTES

CREDITS

Student Edition

ILLUSTRATORS

Cover Garry Colby.

Think Like a Scientist 4–6, 8–9: Garry Colby. 14: Laurie Hamilton. *Borders* Garry Colby.

Unit E 11–12: Higgins Bond. 16–19: Jim Owens. 20–21: Jeffrey Terreson. 26–27: Jenny Campbell. 27: Jackie Geyer. 28–29: Jenny Campbell. 30: Sarah Jane English. 32–33: Jim Salvati. 35: Jackie Geyer. 44–45: Phil Wilson. 48–53: Jenny Campbell. 54–56: Sarah Jane English. 55: Susan Melrath. 61: Jackie Geyer. 62–63: Deborah Pinkney. 64: Jackie Geyer. 66–67: Eldon Doty. 70–71: Tina Fong. 74–75: Robert Schuster. 77: Deborah Pinkney.

Science and Math Toolbox *Logos* Nancy Tobin. 14–15: Andrew Shiff. *Borders* Garry Colby.

Glossary 17–18: Richard Courtney. 19: *b.l.* Dan McGowan. *b.r.* Robert Roper. 20: *t.l.* Richard Courtney. *m.r.* A.J. Miller. 21: *m.l.* Liz Conrad. *m.r.* Jeffrey Terreson. 22–23: Stephen Wagoner. 24: Patrick Gnan. 25: Scott Ross. 26: Denise Davidson. 27: Stephen Wagoner. 28: Pat Gnan. 29 Denise Davidson. 30: *t.l.* Stephen Wagoner. *b.r.* Brad Gaber. 31: Stephen Wagoner.

PHOTOGRAPHS

All photographs by Houghton Mifflin Company (HMCo.) unless otherwise noted.

Cover *t.* NSPI/Mauritius; *m.l.* A & L Sinbaldi/Tony Stone Images; *m.r.* David E. Myers/Tony Stone Images; *b.l.* Gary Vestal/Tony Stone Images; *b.r.* Superstock.

Table of Contents xiv: *l.* © James Steinberg/Photo Researchers, Inc.; *m.* © Gary Retherford/Photo Researchers, Inc.; *r.* Zig Leszczynski/Animals Animals/Earth Scenes.

Think Like a Scientist 4–5: Luiz Claudio Marigo/Peter Arnold, Inc.

Unit E 1: Art Wolfe/Tony Stone Images. 2–3: Art Wolfe/Tony Stone Images. 4–5: Jeff Greenberg/Omni Photo Communications, Inc. 5: Courtesy, Department of the Interior. 7: Grant Huntington for HMCo. 8: Donald Specker/Animals Animals/Earth Scenes. 8–9: Grant Huntington for HMCo. 9: Grant Huntington for HMCo. 10: Doug Perrine/DRK Photo. 11: Al Grotell Underwater Photography. 12: Michael Fogden/DRK Photo. 13: *l.* Stephen J. Krasemann/Peter Arnold, Inc.; *r.* © Dr. Jeremy Burgess/Science Photo Library/Photo Researchers, Inc. 14: Grant Huntington for HMCo. 15: *t.* Grant Huntington for HMCo.; *b.* Grant Huntington for HMCo. 16: *l.* D. Cavagnaro/DRK Photo; *m.* © Farrell Grehan/Photo Researchers, Inc.; *r.* N.H. Cheatham/DRK Photo. 17: *t.* Hans Pfletschinger/Peter Arnold, Inc.; *b.* Jim Brandenburg/Minden Pictures. 18: *t.* © Tim Davis/Photo Researcher, Inc.; *b.* © Tom Bledsoe/Photo Researcher, Inc. 19: *t.* Breck P. Kent/Animals Animals/Earth Scenes; *b.* S. Nielsen/Imagery. 21: *l.* Courtesy, George C. Page Museum; *r.* © Mark Boulton/Photo Researchers, Inc. 22–23: Grant Huntington for HMCo. 23: Grant Huntington for HMCo. 24: Grant Huntington for HMCo. 25: Grant Huntington for HMCo. 26: *l.* © James Steinberg/Photo Researchers, Inc.; *r.* © Gary Retherford/Photo Researchers, Inc.; *r.* Zig Leszczynski/Animals Animals/Earth Scenes. 27: *l.* Ted Levin/Animals Animals/Earth Scenes; *r.* Joe McDonald/Animals Animals/Earth Scenes. 28: *t.l.* Stephen J. Krasemann/DRK Photo; *t.r.* M.P. Kahl/DRK Photo; *b.l.* Stephen Dalton/Animals Animals/Earth Scenes; *b.r.* John Gerlach/Visuals Unlimited. 29: *t.l.* Doug Wechsler/Animals Animals/Earth Scenes; *t.r.* Stephen J. Krasemann/DRK Photo; *m.* Stephen J. Krasemann/DRK Photo; *b.l.* Patrice Ceisel/Visuals Unlimited; *b.r.* Roger Cole/Visuals Unlimited. 30: Australian Picture Library/Leo Meier/Corbis Corporation. 32: © Garry D. McMichael/Photo Researchers, Inc. 34: *l.* © Tim Davis/Photo Researchers, Inc.; *r.* Frans Lanting/Minden Pictures. 36–37: *bkgd.* Kathy Tyrrell/Oxford Scientific Films/Animals Animals/Earth Scenes. 37: *t.* Rhona St.Clair-Moore; *b.* Joe McDonald/Corbis Corporation. 38: Ken Karp for HMCo. 39: Ken Karp for HMCo. 40: © Tom McHugh/Photo Researchers, Inc. 40–41: Dwight Kuhn/DRK Photo. 41: © Anthony Mercieca/Photo Researchers, Inc. 42: © Stephen Dalton/Photo Researchers, Inc. 42–43: Gerry Ellis Nature Photography. 43: © Jeff Lepore/Photo Researchers, Inc. 44–45: © Stephen Dalton/Photo Researchers, Inc. 47: *l.* Ken Karp for HMCo.; *r.* Ken Karp for HMCo. 48: *l.* Hans Pfletschinger/Peter Arnold, Inc.; *m.* John Cancalosi/DRK Photo; *r.* John R. MacGregor/Peter Arnold, Inc. 48–49: Stephen J. Krasemann/Peter Arnold, Inc. 49: *t.* Grant Huntington for HMCo.; *b.* © John Kaprielian/Photo Researchers, Inc. 50: *t.* © Alan Carey/Photo Researchers, Inc.; *b.l.* Marty Snyderman Productions; *b.r.* Marty Snyderman Productions. 51: *t.l.* J. Krasemann/DRK Photo; *t.r.* © Kjell B. Sandved/Photo Researchers, Inc.; *b.l.* © Gregory G. Dimijian M.D./Photo Researchers, Inc.; *b.r.* © S.L. & J.T. Collins/Photo Researchers, Inc. 52: *t.* © William & Marcia Levy/Photo Researchers, Inc. 53: *t.* Stephen J. Krasemann/DRK Photo; *b.* Larry Tackett/Tom Stack & Associates. 54: *r.* Don & Pat Valenti/DRK Photo. 55: Lois Robin. 56: *r.* Gunter Ziesler/Peter Arnold, Inc. 57: Zig Leszczynski/Animals Animals/Earth Scenes. 58–59: *bkgd.* Michael Fogden/DRK Photo; *inset* Luiz Claudio Marigo. 59: Luiz Claudio Marigo. 60: Library of Congress/Corbis Corporation. 65: *l.* Mike Medici/Sonlight Images; *r.* Mark Wilson/Wildshot. 69: Grant Huntington for HMCo. 70–71: Jim Brandenburg/Minden Pictures. 71: William E. Ferguson. 72: John Gerlach/Visuals Unlimited. 72–73: Tom Till/The Wildlife Collection. 73: © Karl H. Switak/Photo Researchers, Inc. 74: John Gerlach/Visuals Unlimited. 75: *t.* Breck P. Kent Photography; *b.* © Mark Rollo/Photo Researchers, Inc. 76: *t.* John Shaw/Tom Stack & Associates; *b.* Joe Devenney/The Image Bank. 79: © Mark Rollo/Photo Researchers, Inc.

Teaching Guide

ILLUSTRATORS

Cover Garry Colby.

Contributing Artists Garry Colby, Jackie Geyer, Deborah Pinkney, Nancy Tobin.

PHOTOGRAPHS

All photographs by Houghton Mifflin Company (HMCo.) unless otherwise noted.

T2–T3: Dan Levinski/Masterfile Corporation. T3: J. Carmichael/The Image Bank. 1: Art Wolfe/Toney Stone Images. 1e: *l.* Stephen J. Krasemann/DRK Photo; *r.* Michael Fogden/DRK Photo. 1f: *t.l.* Courtesy, Sr. Sharon Kassing; *t.r.* Courtesy, Patricia Ramsey; *b.* Courtesy, Shirley Hall. 1q: © Disney. 1r: *bkgd.* PhotoDisc, Inc. 1s: Grant Huntington for HMCo.

SCIENCE and MATH TOOLBOX

H1

Using a
Hand Lens

A hand lens is a tool that magnifies objects, or makes objects appear larger. This makes it possible for you to see details of an object that would be hard to see without the hand lens.

▲ Place the lens above the object.

▲ Move the lens slowly toward you.

Look at a Coin or a Stamp

1. Place an object such as a coin or a stamp on a table or other flat surface.

2. Hold the hand lens just above the object. As you look through the lens, slowly move the lens away from the object. Notice that the object appears to get larger.

3. Keep moving the lens until the object begins to look a little blurry. Then move the hand lens a little closer to the object until the object is once again in sharp focus.

If the object starts to look blurry, move the lens toward the object. ▶

Making a
Bar Graph

A bar graph helps you organize and compare data.

Make a Bar Graph of Animal Heights

Animals come in all different shapes and sizes. You can use the information in the table to make a bar graph of animal heights.

Heights of Animals	
Animal	**Height (cm)**
Bear	240
Elephant	315
Cow	150
Giraffe	570
Camel	210
Horse	165

1. Draw the side and the bottom of the graph. Label the side of the graph as shown. The numbers will show the height of the animals in centimeters.

3. Choose a title for your graph. Your title should describe the subject of the graph.

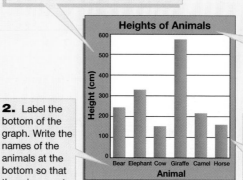

2. Label the bottom of the graph. Write the names of the animals at the bottom so that there is room to draw the bars.

4. Draw bars to show the height of each animal. Some heights are between two numbers.

Using a
Hand Lens

Helpful Hints Hand lenses are listed as 3X, 6X, 8X, etc. This means that the usual maximum magnification is, in the case of the 3X, 3 times the size of the object. In order to attain the greatest magnification, the lens must be held away from the eye.

Try It Out

• Have your students inspect a sheet of graph paper with a hand lens. When the squares are as large as possible, how many squares do they see? How many squares can they see when the lens is held near the eye?

• Placing one lens directly on top of an identical lens doubles the magnification. Have your students try it. Can they find Lincoln's Statue in the Lincoln Memorial on a penny? Can they find the designer's initials under Lincoln's shoulder on the face of the penny?

Making a
Bar Graph

Helpful Hints A good bar graph always has a title and horizontal and vertical axes that are labeled to show what they represent. The label at the base of each bar may be a word or a symbol. If it is a symbol, the graph should include a Key or Legend that tells what each symbol means. If the axis parallel to the bars shows relative numbers, it should be scaled from zero at its base. If it shows measurements, the unit of measure (e.g., cm) should appear in parentheses near the axis label. Bars may be oriented in either a horizontal or vertical direction. The choice of direction may make the graph more meaningful.

Try It Out

• Bar graphs are best used for representing categories that do not have continuous values. Have students prepare bar graphs representing the number of students in each grade in the school.

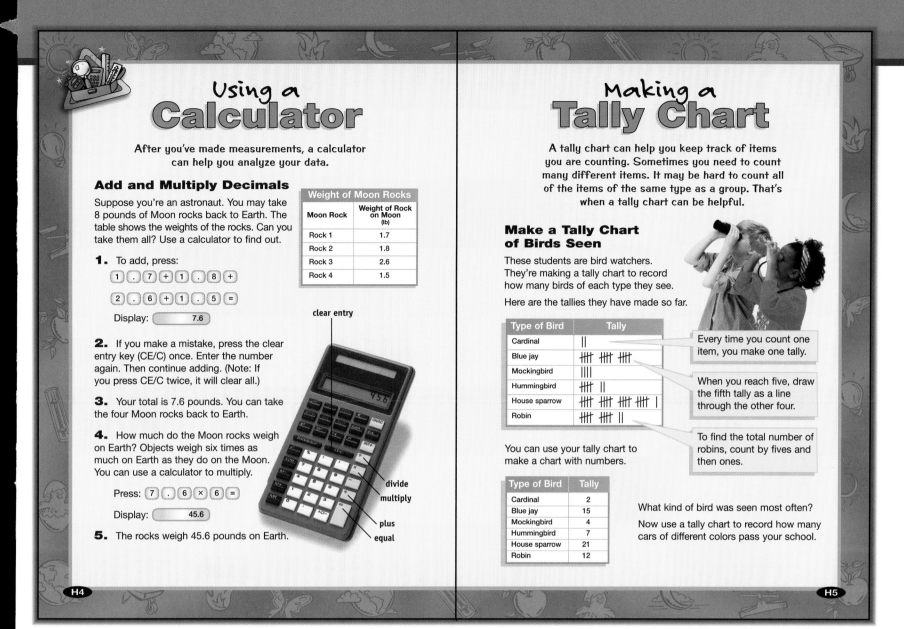

Using a Calculator

After you've made measurements, a calculator can help you analyze your data.

Add and Multiply Decimals

Suppose you're an astronaut. You may take 8 pounds of Moon rocks back to Earth. The table shows the weights of the rocks. Can you take them all? Use a calculator to find out.

Weight of Moon Rocks	
Moon Rock	Weight of Rock on Moon (lb)
Rock 1	1.7
Rock 2	1.8
Rock 3	2.6
Rock 4	1.5

1. To add, press:

1 . 7 + 1 . 8 +

2 . 6 + 1 . 5 =

Display: 7.6

2. If you make a mistake, press the clear entry key (CE/C) once. Enter the number again. Then continue adding. (Note: If you press CE/C twice, it will clear all.)

3. Your total is 7.6 pounds. You can take the four Moon rocks back to Earth.

4. How much do the Moon rocks weigh on Earth? Objects weigh six times as much on Earth as they do on the Moon. You can use a calculator to multiply.

Press: 7 . 6 × 6 =

Display: 45.6

5. The rocks weigh 45.6 pounds on Earth.

clear entry

divide
multiply
plus
equal

Making a Tally Chart

A tally chart can help you keep track of items you are counting. Sometimes you need to count many different items. It may be hard to count all of the items of the same type as a group. That's when a tally chart can be helpful.

Make a Tally Chart of Birds Seen

These students are bird watchers. They're making a tally chart to record how many birds of each type they see.

Here are the tallies they have made so far.

Type of Bird	Tally
Cardinal	‖
Blue jay	卌 卌 卌
Mockingbird	‖‖‖
Hummingbird	卌 ‖
House sparrow	卌 卌 卌 卌 ‖
Robin	卌 卌 ‖

Every time you count one item, you make one tally.

When you reach five, draw the fifth tally as a line through the other four.

To find the total number of robins, count by fives and then ones.

You can use your tally chart to make a chart with numbers.

Type of Bird	Tally
Cardinal	2
Blue jay	15
Mockingbird	4
Hummingbird	7
House sparrow	21
Robin	12

What kind of bird was seen most often?

Now use a tally chart to record how many cars of different colors pass your school.

Using a Calculator

Helpful Hints Calculators are great tools but they have one fault. They always give an answer. However, if one pushes the wrong button… Try to get your students in the habit of always checking to see that the result shown on the calculator display is reasonable.

Try It Out

• Divide the class into groups of about six students. Have each group member trace an outline of his or her shoe on a sheet of paper and cut it out. Within groups measure the length of each shoe in centimeters. If placed end-to-end, how far will the shoe outlines reach? Use the calculator to find the total length.

• Record each group's total length on the chalkboard. Have the groups use calculators to find the total length of all the feet.

Making a Tally Chart

Helpful Hints Tally Charts are useful for collecting any kind of data that involves a count. A tally chart should have a title, a column to list the things being tallied, and a column in which to make tally marks.

Try It Out

• When we are sitting quietly and breathing normally, how many times do we inhale in a minute? Have students tally their inhalations while you keep time. Establish groups with a spread of, say five inhalations, between the highest and the lowest values. Each student can make a tally chart that groups the data. What is the most common range in the class?

• What color automobile is most popular? Students in teams of two can watch traffic, perhaps from a classroom window, while one calls out the colors as cars pass by, the other can keep a tally chart.

Using a Tape Measure or Ruler

Tape measures and rulers are tools for measuring the length of objects and distances. Scientists most often use units such as meters, centimeters, and millimeters when making length measurements.

Use a Tape Measure

1. Measure the distance around a jar. Wrap the tape around the jar.

2. Find the line where the tape begins to wrap over itself.

3. Record the distance around the jar to the nearest centimeter.

Use a Metric Ruler

1. Measure the length of your shoe. Place the ruler or the meterstick on the floor. Line up the end of the ruler with the heel of your shoe.

2. Notice where the other end of your shoe lines up with the ruler.

3. Look at the scale on the ruler. Record the length of your shoe to the nearest centimeter and to the nearest millimeter.

Measuring Volume

A graduated cylinder, a measuring cup, and a beaker are used to measure volume. Volume is the amount of space something takes up. Most of the containers that scientists use to measure volume have a scale marked in milliliters (mL).

Measure the Volume of a Liquid

1. Measure the volume of juice. Pour some juice into a measuring container.

2. Move your head so that your eyes are level with the top of the juice. Read the scale line that is closest to the surface of the juice. If the surface of the juice is curved up on the sides, look at the lowest point of the curve.

3. Read the measurement on the scale. You can estimate the value between two lines on the scale.

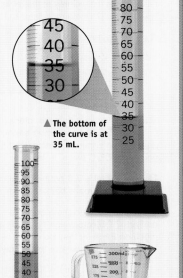

▲ The bottom of the curve is at 35 mL.

This beaker has marks for each 25 mL. ▶

This graduated cylinder has marks for every 1 mL. ▶

▲ This measuring cup has marks for each 25 mL.

Using a Tape Measure or Ruler

Helpful Hints Tape measures often have ends that are ragged or deformed. Such tape measures may still be used by measuring from the one centimeter mark, and then subtracting one from the result. Occasionally, rulers suffer from the same problem.

Try It Out

• Measuring round or irregularly shaped objects is often a problem. Have your students measure the diameter of a ball. Challenge them to devise an accurate method. The easiest way to do it is to place the ball between two vertical planes, such as two books. Then measure the distance between the planes.

Measuring Volume

Helpful Hints Containers that are graduated to measure volume always have a range of error. (In fact, the same can be said for all measuring instruments.) Usually, the smaller the diameter of the container, the more accurate it is. Graduated cylinders are much more accurate than measuring cups designed for the kitchen. Beakers that have graduations on the sides are only approximate.

Try It Out

• Have students use a measuring cup to find the volume of a liquid. Then have them use a graduated cylinder to determine the volume again. Have students discuss the reason for any difference.

Using a
Thermometer

A thermometer is used to measure temperature. When the liquid in the tube of a thermometer gets warmer, it expands and moves farther up the tube. Different scales can be used to measure temperature, but scientists usually use the Celsius scale.

Measure the Temperature of a Cold Liquid

1. Take a chilled liquid out of the refrigerator. Half fill a cup with the liquid.

2. Hold the thermometer so that the bulb is in the center of the liquid. Be sure that there are no bright lights or direct sunlight shining on the bulb.

3. Wait a few minutes until you see the liquid in the tube of the thermometer stop moving. Read the scale line that is closest to the top of the liquid in the tube. The thermometer shown reads 21°C (about 70°F).

Using a
Balance

A balance is used to measure mass. Mass is the amount of matter in an object. To find the mass of an object, place it in the left pan of the balance. Place standard masses in the right pan.

Measure the Mass of a Ball

1. Check that the empty pans are balanced, or level with each other. When balanced, the pointer on the base should be at the middle mark. If it needs to be adjusted, move the slider on the back of the balance a little to the left or right.

2. Place a ball on the left pan. Then add standard masses, one at a time, to the right pan. When the pointer is at the middle mark again, each pan holds the same amount of matter and has the same mass.

3. Add the numbers marked on the masses in the pan. The total is the mass of the ball in grams.

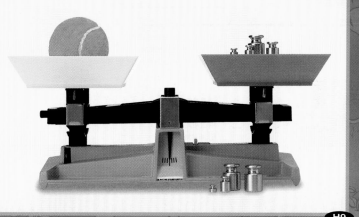

Using a
Thermometer

Helpful Hints When using a thermometer to measure the temperature of a liquid, the thermometer should be read with the bulb still immersed in the liquid. Otherwise, the liquid in the bulb will begin to expand or contract immediately after it is removed.

When measuring air temperatures, students have a tendency to hold the bottom of the thermometer. In order not to affect the reading, they should keep their fingers well away from the bulb.

Try It Out

• Divide your class into groups. Give each group equal volumes of warm and cold water in plastic foam cups. Have each group measure the temperature of the water in both cups. Then have them predict the temperature of the water when combined. Have students try it. The resulting temperature will be halfway between the two.

Using a
Balance

Helpful Hints Teach students to place the object they are measuring on the left-hand pan. Then they will not have a problem when they later encounter balances that have a mass that slides from left to right.

After the balance has been zero adjusted, it should not be moved. Another location might cause the pointer to move off zero.

Try It Out

• Do some paper towels absorb more water than others? Since water has mass, and so do paper towels, the balance is a good instrument to use in determining the answer. Have your students, in teams, design an experiment to solve the problem.

Making a
Chart to Organize Data

A chart can help you keep track of information. When you organize information, or data, it is easier to read, compare, or classify it.

Classifying Animals

Suppose you are studying characteristics of different animals. You want to organize the data that you collect.

Look at the data below. To put this data in a chart, you could base the chart on the two characteristics listed—the number of wings and the number of legs.

My Data

Fleas have no wings. Fleas have six legs.

Snakes have no wings or legs.

A bee has four wings. It has six legs.

Spiders never have wings. They have eight legs.

A dog has no wings. It has four legs.

Birds have two wings and two legs.

A cow has no wings. It has four legs.

A butterfly has four wings. It has six legs.

Give the chart a title that describes the data in it.

Name categories, or groups, that describe the data you have collected.

Make sure the information is recorded correctly in each column.

Animals—Number of Wings and Legs

Animal	Number of Wings	Number of Legs
Flea	0	6
Snake	0	0
Bee	4	6
Spider	0	8
Dog	0	4
Bird	2	2
Cow	0	4
Butterfly	4	6

Next, you could make another chart to show animal classification based on number of legs only.

Reading a
Circle Graph

A circle graph shows a whole divided into parts. You can use a circle graph to compare the parts to each other. You can also use it to compare the parts to the whole.

A Circle Graph of Fuel Use

This circle graph shows fuel use in the United States. The graph has 10 equal parts, or sections. Each section equals $\frac{1}{10}$ of the whole. One whole equals $\frac{10}{10}$.

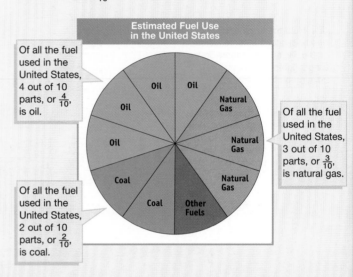

Estimated Fuel Use in the United States

Of all the fuel used in the United States, 4 out of 10 parts, or $\frac{4}{10}$, is oil.

Of all the fuel used in the United States, 3 out of 10 parts, or $\frac{3}{10}$, is natural gas.

Of all the fuel used in the United States, 2 out of 10 parts, or $\frac{2}{10}$, is coal.

Making a
Chart to Organize Data

Helpful Hints When children do science experiments, they should always make data charts to record their observations. The chart might be kept by individual students, a working group, or you. In any case, the chart, or table, should have a title, columns for data, and column headers that tell what data is in each column. If a column in a chart contains measurements, the unit of measure should appear in the column header. This eliminates the need to write the unit after each measurement in the column.

Try It Out

• If you have a computer with a spreadsheet program, have students set up their data charts on the spreadsheet. If you aggregate data from teams following a science activity, you might consider having one or two students input the data as it is reported. Then duplicate the class data for each student.

Reading a
Circle Graph

Helpful Hints Circle graphs make it easy to compare subsets of data. Because data has to be converted to degrees or fractions, circle graphs can be more difficult to prepare than bar graphs. At this age, the emphasis should be on interpreting circle graphs.

Try It Out

• Collect circle graphs from news magazines and newspapers. Distribute them and ask students to write descriptions of what they show. Discuss the advantages of circle graphs over a written paragraph.

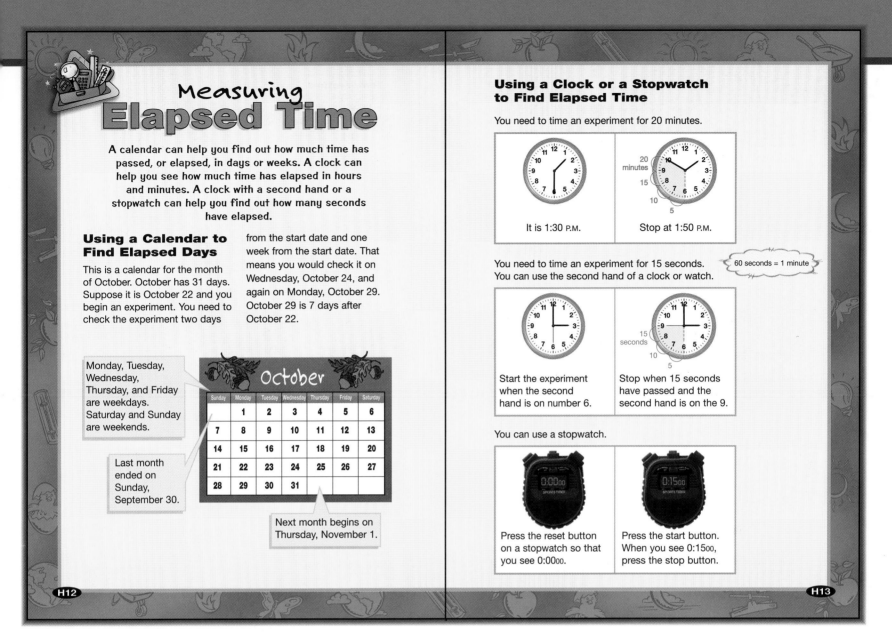

Measuring Elapsed Time

A calendar can help you find out how much time has passed, or elapsed, in days or weeks. A clock can help you see how much time has elapsed in hours and minutes. A clock with a second hand or a stopwatch can help you find out how many seconds have elapsed.

Using a Calendar to Find Elapsed Days

This is a calendar for the month of October. October has 31 days. Suppose it is October 22 and you begin an experiment. You need to check the experiment two days from the start date and one week from the start date. That means you would check it on Wednesday, October 24, and again on Monday, October 29. October 29 is 7 days after October 22.

Monday, Tuesday, Wednesday, Thursday, and Friday are weekdays. Saturday and Sunday are weekends.

Last month ended on Sunday, September 30.

October

Sunday	Monday	Tuesday	Wednesday	Thursday	Friday	Saturday
	1	2	3	4	5	6
7	8	9	10	11	12	13
14	15	16	17	18	19	20
21	22	23	24	25	26	27
28	29	30	31			

Next month begins on Thursday, November 1.

Using a Clock or a Stopwatch to Find Elapsed Time

You need to time an experiment for 20 minutes.

It is 1:30 P.M.   Stop at 1:50 P.M.

You need to time an experiment for 15 seconds. You can use the second hand of a clock or watch.

60 seconds = 1 minute

Start the experiment when the second hand is on number 6.

Stop when 15 seconds have passed and the second hand is on the 9.

You can use a stopwatch.

Press the reset button on a stopwatch so that you see 0:00₀₀.

Press the start button. When you see 0:15₀₀, press the stop button.

Measuring Elapsed Time

Helpful Hints Estimating time intervals is difficult for many people. In many science experiments, an accurate measurement of how long an event took to occur is an important piece of data. Emphasize with students that finding elapsed time is part of data collection in science.

Try It Out

- Use your classroom clock to determine the time elapsed since the school day started, until recess, and so on. Ask students which is easier for figuring elapsed time, a clock with a circular dial or a digital clock?

- How much time must elapse before your next school holiday? Students could number, in reverse order, days on a calendar from that date.

MEASUREMENTS

Volume
1 L of sports drink is a little more than 1 qt.

Area
A basketball court covers about 4,700 ft². It covers about 435 m².

Temperature
The temperature at an indoor basketball game might be 25°C, which is 77°F.

Length/Distance
A basketball rim is about 10 ft high, or a little more than 3 m from the floor.

Mass and Weight
A basketball has a mass of about 650 g. It weighs about 1½ lb.

Metric Measures

Temperature
Ice melts at 0 degrees Celsius (°C)
Water freezes at 0°C
Water boils at 100°C

Length and Distance
1,000 meters (m) = 1 kilometer (km)
100 centimeters (cm) = 1 m
10 millimeters (mm) = 1 cm

Force
1 newton (N) =
   1 kilogram x meter/second/second
   (kg x m/s²)

Volume
1 cubic meter (m³) = 1 m x 1 m x 1 m
1 cubic centimeter (cm³) =
   1 cm x 1 cm x 1 cm
1 liter (L) = 1,000 milliliters (mL)
1 cm³ = 1 mL

Area
1 square kilometer (km²) = 1 km x 1 km
1 hectare = 10,000 m²

Mass
1,000 grams (g) = 1 kilogram (kg)
1,000 milligrams (mg) = 1 g

Customary Measures

Temperature
Ice melts at 32 degrees Fahrenheit (°F)
Water freezes at 32°F
Water boils at 212°F

Length and Distance
12 inches (in.) = 1 foot (ft)
3 ft = 1 yard (yd)
5,280 ft = 1 mile (mi)

Weight
16 ounces (oz) = 1 pound (lb)
2,000 pounds = 1 ton (T)

Volume of Fluids
8 fluid ounces (fl oz) = 1 cup (c)
2 c = 1 pint (pt)
2 pt = 1 quart (qt)
4 qt = 1 gallon (gal)

Metric and Customary Rates
km/h = kilometers per hour
m/s = meters per second
mph = miles per hour

MEASUREMENTS

It is usually not a good idea to ask students to convert values from one measuring system to another. When metric measurements are required, use metric tools; similarly, when customary measurements are needed, use the appropriate instruments. However, some relational benchmarks are useful. For example:

1 cm . . . . is a generous . . . . 1/2 inch
1 meter . . . . is a generous . . . . 1 yard
1 liter . . . . is a generous . . . . . . 1 quart
1 kilogram . . . . . is a generous . . . . . 2 pounds
1 kilometer . . . . . is a generous . . . . 1/2 mile

Room temperature is about 20˚C.
Hot tap water is usually about 40˚C.

If conversions are necessary, use a simple graph to do it. For a temperature conversion, make a graph with Celsius temperatures on one axis and Fahrenheit on the other. Locate and mark two points using these temperatures as coordinates: (0˚C, 32˚F) and (100˚C, 212˚F).

Then draw a straight line through both points. To convert from one temperature scale to another, read across (or up) from one axis to the line and then down (or across) to the other axis. The same technique may be used with length, mass, or volume. All that is needed are two points to establish the line.

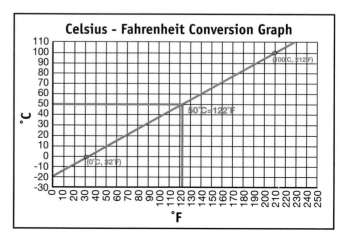

Celsius - Fahrenheit Conversion Graph

GLOSSARY

Pronunciation Key

Symbol	Key Words	Symbol	Key Words
a	cat	g	get
ā	ape	h	help
ä	cot, car	j	jump
		k	kiss, call
e	ten, berry	l	leg
ē	me	m	meat
		n	nose
i	fit, here	p	put
ī	ice, fire	r	red
		s	see
ō	go	t	top
ô	fall, for	v	vat
oi	oil	w	wish
ơ	look, pull	y	yard
o͞o	tool, rule	z	zebra
ou	out, crowd		
		ch	chin, arch
u	up	ŋ	ring, drink
ʉ	fur, shirt	sh	she, push
		th	thin, truth
ə	a in ago	*th*	then, father
	e in agent	zh	measure
	i in pencil		
	o in atom		A heavy stress mark (′) is placed after a syllable that gets a heavy, or primary, stress, as in **picture** (pik′chər).
	u in circus		
b	bed		
d	dog		
f	fall		

A

acid rain (as′id rān) Rain that contains a large amount of acids, and that results from the burning of fossil fuels. (D43) *Acid rain* can harm living things.

adaptation (ad əp tā′shən) Behavior or part of a living thing that helps it survive in a certain environment. (A28, E40) A rose's thorns and a camel's hump are *adaptations*.

adult (ə dult′) The last stage of a life cycle. (A23) The butterfly is the *adult* stage of a caterpillar.

air pollution (er pə lo͞o′shən) Any harmful or unclean materials in the air. (D17) Burning fuels can cause *air pollution*.

aquifer (ak′wə fər) An underground layer of rock where ground water collects. (D31) The water in a well usually comes from an *aquifer*.

astronomer (ə strän′ə mər) A scientist who studies the origin, features, and motion of objects in space. (B14) *Astronomers* use telescopes, cameras, and space probes to study the stars.

atmosphere (at′məs fir) The layer of gases surrounding Earth or another planet. (B12, D8) Earth's *atmosphere* is made up of gases such as oxygen, nitrogen, and carbon dioxide.

atom (at′əm) The smallest particle of matter. (C20) Water is made up of the *atoms* of two different substances—hydrogen and oxygen.

axis (ak′sis) The imaginary line on which an object rotates. (B38) Earth's *axis* runs between the North Pole and the South Pole.

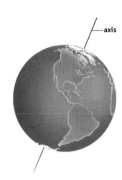

axis

B

behavior (bē hāv′yər) The way an animal typically acts in a certain situation. (E42) One *behavior* of pill bugs is to move toward moist, dark places.

C

camouflage (kam′ə fläzh) The ability to blend in with the surroundings. (E45) An animal's fur or skin can be *camouflage*, helping the animal hunt or avoid hunters.

carnivore (kär′nə vôr) An animal that eats only other animals. (E17) Wolves, cougars, lions, hawks, and owls are *carnivores*.

chemical change (kem′i kəl chānj) A change in matter in which different kinds of matter are formed. (C23) A *chemical change* occurs when wood burns and becomes gases and ash.

chemical property (kem′i kəl präp′ər tē) A description of how matter can change into another kind of matter. (C14) A *chemical property* of paper is its ability to burn.

community (kə myo͞o′nə tē) A group of plants and animals that live in a certain area and depend on one another. (E31) A pond's plants and animals form a *community*.

complete metamorphosis (kəm plēt′ met ə môr′fə sis) The four-stage life cycle of many insects. (A23) A life cycle that goes from egg to larva to pupa to adult is described as a *complete metamorphosis*.

compound machine (kam-pound mə shēn′) A machine that is made up of two or more simple machines. (C76) A pair of scissors is a *compound machine* because it contains two kinds of simple machines—a lever and a wedge.

condense (kən dens′) To change form from a gas to a liquid. (C55, D29) When water vapor in the air cools, it *condenses* into tiny droplets of liquid water.

conduction (kən duk′shən) The movement of heat by direct contact between particles of matter. (C47) Heat moves by *conduction* from warmer matter with faster-moving particles to cooler matter with slower-moving particles.

conductor (kən duk′tər) A material that transfers heat or electricity easily. (C48) Metals are good *conductors* of heat.

cone (kōn) The part of a conifer that produces pollen or seeds. (A50) Each *cone* is a woody stalk covered with stiff scales.

constellation (kän stə lā′shən) A group of stars that form a pattern that looks like a person, animal, or object. (B46) Different *constellations* are visible from Earth at different times of year.

consumer (kən so͞om′ər) A living thing that eats other living things to survive. (E17) Animals are *consumers*.

controlled experiment (kən-trōld′ ek sper′ə mənt) A test of a hypothesis in which the setups are identical in all ways except one. (S7) In the *controlled experiment*, one beaker of water contained salt; all the other beakers contained only water.

convection (kən vek′shən) The circulation of heat through a liquid or gas (fluid) by the movements of particles from one part of the matter to another. (C48) *Convection* takes place in a room with a heater: As hot air rises from the heater, cool air flows down to take its place.

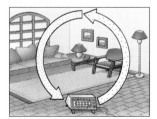

crater (krāt'ər) A bowl-shaped pit. (B11) *Craters* on the Moon and on Earth were formed by meteorites striking the surface.

D

decomposer (dē kəm pōz'ər) A living thing that breaks down and feeds on the remains of once-living things. (E18) *Decomposers* such as mushrooms recycle the remains of once-living things.

dormancy (dôr'mən sē) A decrease in plant activity during the winter. (E76) Sap flows in maple trees in the spring after the tree's *dormancy* during winter.

E

earthquake (ʉrth'kwāk) A sudden movement of large sections of rock beneath Earth's surface. (D51) Books tumbled from shelves during the *earthquake*.

ecosystem (ek'ō sis təm) A place where living and nonliving things interact. (E64) The animals, plants, and insects in the tops of trees in a rain forest have their own *ecosystem*.

egg (eg) The first stage in the life cycle of almost all animals. (A14) Birds hatch from *eggs* outside the mother bird's body.

embryo (em'brē ō) An animal or plant in the earliest stages of its development. (A15, A39) A plant *embryo* is the tiny plant that is found inside a seed.

energy (en'ər jē) The ability to cause a change in matter. (C31) A car uses *energy* from gasoline or diesel fuel to run.

energy of motion (en'ər jē uv mō'shən) The energy that moving matter has. (C31) Sliding downhill on a sled, tossing a basketball into the air, and flying a kite in the wind are examples of *energy of motion*.

environment (en vī'rən mənt) All the surrounding living and nonliving things that affect a living thing. (E10) A drop of water, a rotting log, a desert, an ocean, and a rain forest are examples of different *environments*.

equator (ē kwāt'ər) An imaginary line that circles Earth halfway between the two poles. (B64) If you live near the *equator*, you live in a hot climate because your region receives direct sunlight most of the time.

North Pole

Equator

South Pole

energy of motion — continued

erosion (ē rō'zhən) The breaking up and moving of weathered rocks from one place to another. (D52) The Grand Canyon was formed by millions of years of *erosion*.

evaporate (ē vap'ə rāt) To change form from a liquid to a gas. (C54, D29) On a warm dry day, puddles on the sidewalk *evaporate* quickly.

extinction (ek stiŋk'shən) The permanent disappearance of all living things of a certain kind. (E20) The *extinction* of the saber-toothed cat is a mystery that some scientists are working to solve.

F

flare (fler) A bright area on the surface of the Sun caused by a solar storm. (B27) A solar *flare* is hotter than surrounding areas of the Sun and so is brighter.

---

food chain (fōōd chān) The path that energy takes through a community as one living thing eats another. (E26) The first link in a *food chain* is usually a plant.

food web (fōōd web) Two or more food chains that overlap and link. (E28) A *food web* connects animals through the plants and animals that they eat.

force (fôrs) A push or a pull. (C64) When you open a door, you apply a *force*.

fossil fuel (fäs'əl fyōō'əl) A fuel formed over time from the remains of plants or animals. (D10) *Fossil fuels* such as oil, coal, and natural gas are found underground.

freeze (frēz) To change form from a liquid to a solid. (C55) The loss of heat causes a liquid to *freeze*.

friction (frik'shən) A force that makes it hard for two objects to move past one another easily when the objects touch. (C46) *Friction* causes your hands to get warm when you rub them together.

fruit (frōōt) The part of a flower that forms around a seed. (A45) Cucumbers, tomatoes, oranges, peaches, and pears are *fruits*.

fulcrum (ful'krəm) The fixed point around which a lever turns. (C73) If you use a lever to lift an object, the *fulcrum* is located between you and the object you are lifting.

G

gas (gas) A state of matter that has no definite shape and does not take up a definite amount of space. (C20) A *gas* spreads out evenly to fill whatever space it is in.

germ (jʉrm) A tiny organism that can cause disease. (D37) Chlorine kills some of the *germs* in water.

germinate (jʉr'mə nāt) To sprout and begin to develop into a seedling. (A40) Most kinds of seeds need moisture, air, and warmth to *germinate*.

glacier (glā'shər) A large mass of slow-moving ice. (D53) When a *glacier* meets the sea, large chunks of ice fall off, forming icebergs.

gravity (grav'i tē) A force that pulls two or more objects toward each other. (B22, C65) To fly into space, a rocket must overcome Earth's *gravity*.

ground water (ground wôt'ər) The water found beneath Earth's surface. (D31) In some areas, *ground water* fills the small spaces that are between underground rocks, soil, and sand.

H

habitat (hab'i tat) The place where an animal or a plant lives. (E10) Deer live in a woodland *habitat*.

heat (hēt) The energy of moving particles of matter. (C32) Adding *heat* to matter causes its particles to move faster.

herbivore (hʉr'bə vôr) An animal that eats only plants. (E18) Cows and rabbits are *herbivores*.

hibernation (hī bər nā'shən) A deep sleep that helps some animals survive the winter. (E75) An animal that is in *hibernation* breathes slowly, has a slow heartbeat, and has a low body temperature.

hypothesis (hī päth'ə sis) An idea about or explanation of how or why something happens. (S6) The *hypothesis* that the Earth revolves around the Sun has been supported by evidence gathered by astronomers.

I

inclined plane (in klīnd' plān) A simple machine with a slanted surface. It allows objects to be raised or lowered from one level to another without lifting them. (C74) A ramp is a kind of *inclined plane*.

incomplete metamorphosis
(in kəm plēt′ met ə môr′fə sis)
The three-stage life cycle of some
insects. (A24) A life cycle that goes
from egg to nymph to adult is
called *incomplete metamorphosis*.

inexhaustible resource (in eg-
zôs′tə bəl rē′sôrs) A natural
resource that does not decrease, or
become used up, as people use it.
(D11) Wind can't be used up so it
is an *inexhaustible resource*.

insulator (in′sə lāt ər) A poor
conductor of heat or electricity.
(C48) Air that is trapped in the
small spaces between fibers of
clothing acts as an *insulator*.

larva (lär′və) The second stage
in the life cycle of an insect that
undergoes complete
metamorphosis. (A23) A butterfly
larva is called a caterpillar.

lava (lä′və) Liquid rock flowing
on the surface. (D51) Fires broke
out when *lava* reached the wooden
frames of houses.

lever (lev′ər) A simple machine
made up of a bar that turns, or
rotates, around a fixed point. (C73)
A *lever* helps to lift a heavy object
or a tight lid with less effort.

life cycle (līf sī′kəl) The
ordered changes that occur during
the lifetime of a living thing. (A9)
An insect goes through three or
four stages in its *life cycle*.

liquid (lik′wid) A state of matter
that has no definite shape but
takes up a definite amount of
space. (C20) At room temperature,
water is a *liquid*.

lunar eclipse (lōō′nər i klips′)
The darkening of the Moon when
it moves into Earth's shadow.
(B76) During a *lunar eclipse*,
Earth blocks the Sun's light from
reaching the Moon directly.

machine (mə shēn′) Something
that makes a task easy to do by
reducing the amount of force
needed to do a job. (C72) A
machine can make it easier to
move, lift, carry, or cut
something.

magma (mag′mə) Liquid rock
deep inside Earth. (D50) After
magma flows out of a volcano the
magma is called lava.

mass (mas) The amount of
matter that something contains.
(C10) An elephant has more *mass*
than an insect.

matter (mat′ər) Anything that
has mass and takes up space. (C10)
Every living and nonliving thing
around you is made of *matter*.

melt (melt) To change form
from a solid to a liquid. (C54) Ice
melts at 0°C (32°F) and iron melts
at 1,530°C (2,786°F).

meteorite (mēt′ē ər īt) A chunk
of rock or metal that has fallen
from space. (B11) A *meteorite*
may be as small as a grain of sand
or as large as a house.

migrate (mī′grāt) To move to
another region as the seasons
change. (E74) Many northern birds
and butterflies *migrate* south
during the winter.

minerals (min′ər əlz) Solids
found in nature that have a definite
chemical makeup. (D10) Calcium is
a *mineral* found in milk and cheese.

natural resource (nach′ər əl
rē′sôrs) A material found in or
on Earth that people use. (D9)
Natural resources include water,
minerals, fossil fuels, soil, plants,
and animals.

nonrenewable resource
(nän ri nōō′ə bəl rē′sôrs) A
natural resource that cannot
be replaced within a person's
lifetime. (D11) Diamonds are
nonrenewable resources because
it will take nature millions of
years to make more.

nutrient (nōō′trē ənt) Any
substance used by living things for
energy, growth, repair, or other life
processes. (E43) Proteins,
carbohydrates, and fats are
nutrients found in food.

nymph (nimf) The second stage
in the life cycle of an insect
undergoing incomplete
metamorphosis. (A24) A
grasshopper *nymph* looks similar
to a small adult.

omnivore (äm′ni vôr) An animal
that eats both plants and animals.
(E18) Because bears will eat both
berries and fish, bears are classified
as *omnivores*.

opaque (ō pāk′) Materials that
block light. (C35) *Opaque* curtains
are used in theaters to block the
light from windows.

orbit (ôr′bit) The path a planet,
moon, or other object takes
around another. (B46) The Moon
is seen in different phases as it
moves through its *orbit* around
Earth.

parasite (par′ə sīt) A living thing
that, at some point in its life, lives
on or in another living thing and
harms it. (E52) Fleas, lice, and some
kinds of worms are *parasites*.

petal (pet′′l) The brightly colored
part of a flower that helps attract
birds, bees, and other insects to
the flower. (A44) A *petal* is one of
the three main parts of a flower.

phase (fāz) Any stage in the
series of changes in the apparent
shape of the Moon. (B53) The
Moon's shape appears to change
with each *phase*.

physical change (fiz′i kəl chānj)
A change in the size, shape, or
state of matter. (C23) When water
freezes, it undergoes a *physical
change* from a liquid to a solid.

physical property (fiz′i kəl
präp′ ər tē) A quality of matter
that can be measured or observed
with the senses without changing
the matter into another kind of
matter. (C14) A *physical property*
of ice is its hardness.

pistil (pis′til) The central part in
a flower where seeds form. (A44)
For seeds to form in a plant, the
pollen must travel to the *pistil*.

planet (plan′it) A large body
that orbits a star and does not
produce light of its own. (B47)
Earth is a *planet*.

pollen (päl′ən) The powdery
grains in a flower; they must be
carried from a stamen to a pistil in
order for seeds to form. (A44)
Bees move *pollen* from one flower
to another.

pollination (päl ə nā′shən) The
process by which pollen reaches a
pistil. (A44) After *pollination*, a
flower can produce seeds.

pollution (pə lōō′shən) Any
unwanted or harmful material
found in the environment. (D17)
Air *pollution* can cause damage to
your lungs.

precipitation (prē sip ə tā′shən)
The liquid or solid forms of water
that fall to Earth. (D31) Rain, sleet,
hail, and snow are different kinds
of *precipitation*.

predator (pred′ə tər) An animal
that hunts other animals for food.
(E27) Hawks, cougars, and sharks
are *predators*.

prey (prā) An animal hunted for
food by another animal. (E27)
Rabbits, mice, small fish, and
insects are often *prey* for larger
animals.

producer (prō dōōs′ər) A living
thing that can make its own food.
(E16) Plants, such as trees and
grass, are *producers*.

prominence (präm′ə nəns) A
huge loop of gas that appears on
the edge of the Sun. (B27)
Prominences are caused by
magnetic storms on the Sun.

property (präp′ər tē) Something that describes matter. (C12) A *property* of water in its liquid form is its ability to flow.

pulley (pool′ē) A wheel around which a rope or chain is passed. (C75) A *pulley* helps lift objects that would be too heavy to lift directly.

pupa (pyoo′pə) The third stage in the life cycle of an insect undergoing complete metamorphosis. (A23) As a *pupa*, an insect is enclosed in a cocoon, or case.

radiation (rā dē ā′shən) The movement of heat energy in the form of waves. (C49) Heat from a campfire reaches you through *radiation*.

renewable resource (ri noo′ə-bəl rē′sôrs) A natural resource that can be replaced within a person's lifetime. (D11) Lumber is a *renewable resource* if new trees are planted to replace cut trees.

reservoir (rez′ər vwär) The body of water that is stored behind a dam. (D31) A *reservoir* stores fresh water for a town or city.

revolve (ri välv′) To move in a circle or orbit. (B46) Earth *revolves* around the Sun.

rotation (rō tā′shən) The spinning motion around an axis. (B38) Earth takes 24 hours to complete one *rotation*.

scale (skāl) A cone's woody part on which seeds grow. (A51) A pine cone's *scales* protect its seeds.

season (sē′zən) Any of the four parts of the year. (B65) The four *seasons* are spring, summer, fall, and winter.

seed coat (sēd kōt) The part of a seed that protects the plant embryo. (A39) The *seed coat* of a coconut is hard, thick, and brown.

seedling (sēd′liŋ) The new plant that develops from an embryo and has roots, a stem, and leaves. (A41) A tomato *seedling* can be started indoors in early spring and planted outside in May.

simple machine (sim′pəl mə shēn′) A device that changes the size or direction of a force. (C73) A lever is a *simple machine*.

soil The loose material that covers much of Earth's surface. (D56) As they grow, most plants extend their roots into *soil*.

solar eclipse (sō′lər i klips′) The blocking of light from the Sun when the Moon moves between it and Earth. (B75) During a *solar eclipse*, the Sun's light is blocked by the Moon.

solar energy (sō′lər en′ər jē) Energy produced by the Sun. (C36) *Solar energy* can be used to produce electricity.

solar system (sō′lər sis′təm) The Sun and all the planets and other objects that orbit it. (B47) Earth is one of nine planets in the *solar system*.

solid (säl′id) A state of matter that has a definite shape and takes up a definite amount of space. (C19, D14) A rock, a piece of ice, and a chair are all examples of *solids*.

species (spē′shēz) A group of living things that can produce living things of the same kind. (A10) The lion *species* cannot produce young of the gorilla *species*.

stamen (stā′mən) The part of a flower that produces pollen, which is needed to form seeds. (A44) *Stamens* are often long and have a fuzzy end.

star (stär) A ball of very hot gases that gives off light and other energy. (B27) The Sun is a *star*.

states of matter (stāts uv mat′r.) The three forms that matter takes—solid, liquid, and gas. (C19) Water exists naturally in all three *states of matter*.

stored energy (stôrd en′ər jē) Energy in matter that can cause matter to move or change. (C31) Fuels have *stored energy* from the Sun.

sunspot (sun′spät) A dark area on the surface of the Sun, caused by a solar storm. (B27) A *sunspot* appears darker because it is cooler than surrounding areas of the Sun.

surface water (sur′fis wôt′ər) Fresh water in lakes, streams, and rivers. (D30) People often pipe *surface water* to nearby cities.

telescope (tel′ə skōp) A device that makes distant objects appear larger and brighter. (B15) A *telescope* is used to study stars and other planets.

temperature (tem′pər ə chər) A measure of how hot or cold something is. (C45) *Temperature* is measured with a thermometer.

theory (thē′ə rē) A hypothesis that is supported by a lot of evidence and is widely accepted by scientists. (S9) The big-bang *theory* offers an explanation for the origin of the universe.

topsoil (täp′ soil) A mixture of weathered rock and humus (decayed plant and animal matter). (D57) *Topsoil* contains nutrients that help plants to grow.

variable (ver′ē ə bəl) The one difference in the setups of a controlled experiment; provides a comparison for testing a hypothesis. (S7) The *variable* in an experiment with plants was the amount of water given each plant.

volcano (väl kā′nō) An opening in the ground through which hot ash, gases, and lava move from inside Earth to the surface, sometimes forming a cone-shaped hill or mountain. (D51) Lava poured out of the *volcano*, adding a new layer of rock to the land.

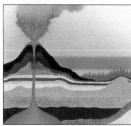

volume (väl yoom) The amount of space that matter takes up. (C11) A *volume* of water that measures a pint weighs about a pound.

water cycle (wôt′ər sī′kəl) The path that water follows as it evaporates into the air, condenses into clouds, and returns to Earth as rain, snow, sleet, or hail. (D30) In the *water cycle*, water evaporates from lakes and oceans into the air, and then condenses and falls back to Earth as rain or snow.

water vapor (wôt′ər vā′pər) Water that is in the form of a gas. (D29) Steam, which is invisible, is *water vapor*.

weathering (weth′ər iŋ) The breaking up or wearing away of rocks. (D52) Rock formations in Arches National Park have been formed by the *weathering* action of wind and rain.

wetlands (wet′landz) Swamps, marshes, and bogs that are home to many kinds of animals and plants. (E65) *Wetlands* are low-lying areas where water is absorbed into underground aquifers.

wheel and axle (hwēl ənd ak′səl) A simple machine that is made up of two wheels that turn together. (C75) A doorknob, along with its shaft, is an example of a *wheel and axle*.

INDEX

*Activity
Bold heads indicate Teaching Guide material.

*Activity
Bold heads indicate Teaching Guide material.

*Activity
Bold heads indicate Teaching Guide material.

*Activity
Bold heads indicate Teaching Guide material.